Nicolas Ca

INDOOR GROWING

The Complete Guide to Indoor Gardening.

Collection of Four Books: Hydroponics, Aquaponics for Beginners, Aeroponics and Greenhouse Gardening.

(All in One)

Nicolas Campos

Contents

Nicolas Campos

Congratulations on purchasing this collection of four books and thank you for doing so. This collection is specially designed for those who want to build an indoor system to grow their own vegetables and ornamental plants at home in a simple and professional way.

Nicolas Campos

Nicolas Campos

Nicolas Campos

HYDROPONICS

DIY Beginner's Guide. How to Build an Inexpensive Hydroponic System at Home and Quickly Start Growing Vegetables, Fruits, and Herbs without Soil

Nicolas Campos

INTRODUCTION

Hydroponics is the method of growing crops without soil, but it provides all the necessary mineral nutrients. The gardener involved in hydroponics is responsible for regulating the composition of the nutrients in the liquid solution he prepares for irrigation of the plants and must also regulate the frequency of this nutrient supply. The good thing is that the entire cultivation process is highly automated, but still requires very close management.

Hydroponics is preferable because it uses water and nutrients efficiently, especially since both are applied directly to the roots of the plant.

The availability of lighting is also an important component in agricultural production. Adequate lighting is achieved by planting crops in vertical structures so that accessibility to light is maximised, while density and shading are kept to a minimum.

These growing conditions for plant cultivation, in terms of water, nutrients and light, are ideal for crops and will maximise the usefulness of the growing area and use space that might otherwise be unused. Having a mobile multi-level cultivation structure exposes plants to ideal lighting always during the growing season.

CHAPTER 1 - Hydroponic Gardening

Meaning and Etymology

What is hydroponics?

We can say that hydroponics is the cultivation of plants above ground, i.e. without soil and thanks to water, in which suitable nutrients are dissolved to make the plants grow fast and healthy. In short, it is the cultivation of plants in water. The etymology of the word hydroponics is to be found in the ancient Greek language: "hydro" meaning water and "ponos" meaning work. The word hydroponics identifies precisely the work and action of water used for the development and cultivation of plants, both decorative and fruit and vegetables.

How hydroponic gardening works

General Information

Hydroponic cultivation is a process that does not use soil to grow plants. Anyone can succeed in growing salad or ornamental plants in a pot with growing medium or in the ground with reasonable success. But to grow the same plants without soil, you need to know in depth how they grow, so you can control light, temperature, water, oxygen and nutrients. These elements are all vital for the health and growth of aubergine or ficus within a hydroponic system.

It seems that we have just described a futuristic technique, taken from a science fiction book or just out of a laboratory in some university. But we haven't. In the Hanging Gardens of Babylon, there were already indications of above-ground cultivation. Growing vegetables or similar in water is an ancient practice used by the Aztec empire, with the Chinampa system. They used it in many places of their great empire, such as in Mexico and on Lake Titicaca, where the locals created, and still do today, floating islands, built entirely with biodegradable materials. Here an optimal habitat is established for the cultivation of plant species, the protection of animals and the purification of water.

In another region of the earth, known for its extreme poverty, we find a similar technique, Vasoman Chash, translated as "floating agriculture". During the monsoon season, most of the structures are destroyed, while these settlements resist and continue to produce. A consolidated platform, formed all by local and low cost raw materials, among which some weeds, for instance the water hyacinths, constitutes the substratum of cultivation entirely organic, also in this case a technique of above ground cultivation very similar to the hydroponic cultivation.

These systems are the precursors of modern cultivation techniques known as the floating system, where plants are bred on floating supports, inside waterproofed containers filled with water, in which the nutrients are dissolved.

In the modern era it was William Frederick Gericke, a professor at the University of California at Berkeley, who published a book on a new technology he thought would lead to the end of the war. His invention, which he called hydroponics, would allow countries at war to produce more food with fewer resources. Underlying these studies were other research conducted since 1860 by the German agricultural chemist W. Knop, who had begun studying how to isolate chemical compounds in the soil to study fertilizers and their use.

How to grow hydroponics

Hydroponic growing systems can have several characteristics that distinguish them and help in the production of a vegetable or ornamental plant. We can have them with or without substrate, with drip irrigation systems or with sub-irrigation, depending on the method used for the supply of the nutritive solution, with open or closed cycle, if the nutritive solution moves in a system that goes outside or not.

In a hydroponic system, a solution of water and nutrients circulates through plant roots and replaces the need for traditional soil and fertilizers. With this science fiction but also very ancient technique, farmers and gardeners can grow food and flowering plants in non-traditional places, such as kitchens and basements, windowsills, balconies and roofs. We know the technology well by now, if you provide the light, water, air and nutrients needed in a well-built system, you will see that you can grow tomatoes, soybeans, lettuce, petunias or geraniums in unimaginable quantities and of good quality.

Hydroponic cultivation also requires a thorough knowledge of chemistry, botany, hydraulics and agriculture.

Now let's see what the main components of a hydroponic system are:

- Watertight containers in which plants are planted.
- Nutrient solution, consisting of water and fertilizers that dissolve easily in water. It serves to give plants the water and substances necessary for their growth. There are many liquid fertilizers on the market. Depending on the plants you want to grow

you will need to find the necessary elements, the right dose and frequency of administration.

- Growing substrate, i.e. the material on which the plants will be grown and where they will take root. There are many alternatives on the market for this purpose: pumice, expanded clay, volcanic lapillus, vermiculite, perlite, coconut fibre, etc. In these compounds the water must be free to run off to prevent the formation of harmful diseases to plants and must offer a good grip to the roots.

- Irrigation system composed of all its individual parts, from the main to the secondary pipelines, to the point drippers, to the electronic control unit for the regulation of flows, times and durations. To build this, it is necessary to have at least a basic knowledge of hydraulics, in order to avoid gross errors and to ensure that everything works correctly.

- Dozer for fertilizer, a simple but indispensable mechanism to create the nutritive solution with the correct percentage of fertilizer dissolved in water.

- Drainage system, necessary to collect the excess nutrient solution in a containment tank and then reuse it later or dispose of it outside.
- Seedlings to be planted. They can be produced by sowing or purchased already of the desired size and then prepared for planting in the new system.

In some methods like hydroponics, the roots of the plants, which are suspended in the air and in the dark, nutrients are distributed by nebulization at regular intervals and with well-defined times. This cultivation technique is called aeroponics or fogponics or misophonic.

Nutrients and oxygen are not the only fundamental elements in plant growth. Light must be available to the plants in precise times and ways, as it is the main component of photosynthesis. Just like the nutrient solution, it is possible to give adequate amounts of light to plants grown with hydroponics with different systems. We can proceed with natural lighting, or alternatively with artificial lighting.

After years of experimentation in the agricultural field and evaluation of costs and benefits brought, hydroponics is becoming more and more successful in different fields: from domestic or hobby to industrial production, to advanced research for space exploration.

In large cities, where there is no possibility to cultivate productive agricultural land, in some cases farms have been built for the production, especially of vegetables, using the technique of hydroponic cultivation, in spaces otherwise unusable for this purpose (urban farming). In the same way, but on a small scale, small domestic gardens can be created everywhere.

In some large cities hydroponic farmers have had the idea of buying space to build their farms with no productive value. They built real vertical farms in spaces like empty warehouses and old containers. Many are convinced that these hydroponic farms can have a positive impact on urban communities by providing fresh, zero-mileage products.

Nicolas Campos

CHAPTER 2 - How Hydroponic Gardening Works

As said, hydroponics is a cultivation technique of ancient origins that uses water to grow plants outside the soil, without them needing the soil.

Growing without soil uses an alternative substrate such as expanded clay, coconut fibre or other substrates or mixtures of these instead of soil. The plant is usually fed with a solution consisting mainly of water and predominantly inorganic mineral elements which are administered to the plants.

Aeroponic cultivation (a type of hydroponic cultivation) involves the cultivation of plants without the use of substrate or any other support aggregate. The plants are in fact artificially supported and their feeding is guaranteed by water misting systems enriched with mineral fertilizers that directly affect the plant's root system and roots.

Hydroponics can also be developed thanks to kits that allow you to create an indoor plant for your above ground cultivation. This new method of cultivation has been developing for a long time in various parts of the world.

What are the advantages of hydroponics?

The cultivation of plants in hydroponics in greenhouses has many advantages and can be used for different purposes, both for personal and professional use.

Foods grown with this technique are not subject to the seasonality of their growth, as I can make the plant believe that it is always springtime, with many hours of sunshine and ideal temperatures. For a hydroponic farm or a hydroponic vegetable garden grown on the kitchen balcony, vegetable production times are reduced. Just think that you can have your basil fresh all year round. The yield of production increases compared to traditional soil-based crops. The quality of the products is on average higher than industrial production.

24

One of the main advantages of hydroponic cultivation is space saving: the hydroponic vegetable garden, thanks to its low weight and the possibility of being easily moved, allows you to grow even in places that cannot normally be exploited, such as vertical walls, which instead become real vegetable gardens, or even on small balconies at home. In fact, you can grow healthy vegetables and vegetables in a simple way without using the land.

Moreover, the water consumption is lower: the water supplied is about one tenth of the water needed for irrigation of a traditional vegetable garden of the same size, thanks to the water recovery and disinfection technologies provided by hydroponic systems. The hydroponic greenhouse is, therefore, a very economical cultivation system because it guarantees a higher growth and production compared to the traditional growth in soil and needs little water, in fact it saves up to 80% thanks to the recovery system compared to open field crops.

A hydroponic growing system, although it is based entirely on water and nutrients dissolved in it, uses about a tenth of the amount of water needed in a gardening or common agricultural activity. This is because water is generally used again in the production cycle.

Plant maintenance in hydroponic plant systems requires less time and less energy. You will not have weeds to weed out all the time, or aphids and mites to fight. The growing environment is controlled, so pests and fungal attacks are also reduced.

Finally, there is more cleanliness: a garden without soil is cleaner and does not carry bacteria and pests. In addition, the environment is not polluted by using pesticides to eradicate plant diseases because neither viruses nor soil bacteria develop as it is absent.

What are the disadvantages of hydroponics?

The biggest disadvantage is the initial planting costs, which are generally higher than those for common cultivation methods. This is mainly for hydroponic farms. In contrast, domestic hydroponic systems can be built with different degrees of complexity and different costs.

From products made with waste elements, such as plastic bottles, to others made with cut plastic tubes used as containers, to those using specially made components. In the experimentation of this way of cultivation, you can go from the small package to be installed on the window sill to the more complex one that requires the construction of a dedicated greenhouse with complex systems of lighting, irrigation and regulation of temperature and related air flows.

In all these cases, as anticipated, the necessary knowledge is above average. But no one forbids experimentation. But I remind you that if you want to try, always check that there is power in the house. Without it the light goes out and the irrigation stops. A real disaster. If you use your garage or cellar, remember that electricity costs can go up a lot. However, technological innovations are ongoing, and the ingenuity is becoming increasingly sharp when it comes to consumption.

Indoor and outdoor hydroponics

In agriculture, above-ground farming systems are becoming increasingly widespread globally. This is because these techniques offer many advantages and allow the cultivation of many types of plants even where there are adverse conditions for agriculture.

Hydroponics, moreover, allows producers to grow large quantities of vegetables, maintaining (and in many cases improving) the quality and organoleptic characteristics of garden products.

The hydroponic system, in its simplicity, is also ideal for domestic crops and is effective for both gardening and vegetable garden cultivation.

Hydroponics is based on the interaction of certain materials and factors:

- pH-neutral substrate.
- constant humidity.
- balanced plant nutrition.

These are the principles on which the success of hydroponics is based.

Hydroponics is very versatile and is suitable for both vegetables and ornamental plants. This system can also be used for both indoor and outdoor cultivation.

In the garden, in pots on the terrace, or on the balcony, the hydroponic system allows you to grow a wide variety of plants, optimizing resources and achieving great results.

Simply replace the soil or potting soil with the substrate and you can create your own tailor-made garden or vegetable garden.

The substrate can consist of:

- expanded clay.
- coconut fibre.

The advantage is that it supports the plants, guaranteeing the passage of air and the right oxygenation of the roots, and keeping the humidity level constant without damaging water stagnation.

The substrate must be regularly irrigated (by hand or with an automated system) with water to which fertilizers are added. Naturally, each type of crop has its own specific needs for which there are several products to be diluted in the liquid.

In outdoor hydroponic cultivation it is necessary to know the needs of the plants in terms of exposure to the sun and their climatic preferences.

Indoors, on the other hand, the hydroponic system offers the added advantage of controlling lighting and temperature variables. With the kits for hydroponic greenhouses complete with LED lamp, you can create a small ecosystem that works perfectly, thanks to the synergy of all internal factors.

What are the Advantages of Indoor Growing?

The hydroponic greenhouse for indoor growing allows you to create a green corner, with ornamental or vegetable garden plants, in any domestic environment and of dimensions tailored to your space requirements.

The hydroponic greenhouse for domestic use works more or less like those for commercial use: it recreates the ideal conditions for the growth and development of plants, which will no longer be subject to the seasonality of the vegetative phases and will enjoy a longer and healthier life cycle.

This technique, in fact, without subjecting the plants to any kind of stress, guarantees them to grow healthy and luxuriant.

In addition, with the right amount of fertilizers for plant nutrition, it has been shown that flowering and vegetable production reach an excellent level of quality.

Many are the advantages of indoor growing with the hydroponic system:

- plants that flourish all year round.
- constant production of fruit and vegetables.
- cleanliness and hygiene of the system.
- absence of pests, weeds, mould and fungi.

The small ecosystem is designed to keep the chosen plants healthy and productive, but some control tools may be useful:

- measure pH and CE values.
- measure moisture values.

Each crop, as said, has special needs and each greenhouse can be equipped with instruments or accessories that make the system efficient for all specific cases.

Once the hydroponic greenhouse cultivation has started, keeping the seedlings healthy and productive is an easy operation that does not require any special care.

Which plants can be grown indoors?

Thanks to the versatility of the hydroponic growing technique, it is possible to grow many plants, both ornamental and garden plants.

Among the ornamental plants, green leaf and flowering plants, the most suitable are:

- ficus.
- pothos.
- dracaena.
- pholodendron and similar.
- hibiscus.

- anthurium spathipphyllum.
- epiphytic orchids.
- saintpaulia and the like.

With these types of plants, it is possible to create small green and flowery oases that give a lot of satisfaction, cheering up the domestic environment even during the long city winters.

Hydroponics is also an excellent solution for the cultivation of a small domestic garden with vegetables and aromatic and medicinal herbs. For example:

- tomatoes.
- cucumbers.
- aubergines.
- all green leafy salad vegetables.
- hot pepper.
- basil.
- sage.
- rosemary.
- edible flowers and many more.

With hydroponic cultivation, the products of the garden are available all year round and ready to use in the kitchen or for the preparation of infusions or healthy decoctions.

Indoor hydroponics is also an eco-sustainable choice for several reasons:

- reduced water consumption.
- absence or reduced use of pesticides.
- production of genuine vegetables and vegetables.

The hydroponic greenhouse garden, finally, is also an educational experience for children who will enthusiastically witness the miracle of nature: from the germination of seeds, to the growth of seedlings, to the production of vegetables, vegetables and aromatic herbs, with a genuine taste and many beneficial properties for our health.

You can create your own garden or indoor garden in every room of the house: in the kitchen, on the veranda, in the living room or wherever you prefer. The system, in the automated version, does not need any kind of superstructure and consumes little energy; on the contrary, it allows you to save on water consumption for irrigation. The result is guaranteed and the benefit you get from it, also in terms of psychophysical well-being, is immediately evident.

What are the materials to use for the substrate?

An effective soil-free cultivation system is the result of the application of a series of precise technical measures, which aim to create optimal conditions for the life and health of plants.

The nutrient solution will consist of water and water-soluble fertilizer, with the aim of providing water and nutrients to the plants. It can be prepared from a complete commercial fertilizer (with macronutrients N, P, K, Ca, MG, S but also, to a lesser extent, micronutrients Cu, Fe, B, Mo, and Mn), of the type normally found in supermarkets and DIY/gardening stores. The dosage, based on the concentrations normally used in these products, is about 1-1.5 g/litre, which can be increased when deficiency symptoms appear (e.g. yellowing of the leaves), or decreased when excess occurs (e.g. with burns on the leaf flaps due to saline stress), or in warmer periods.

The growing medium consists of the material in which the roots of the plant will develop. The substrates used in cultivation without soil in general are different, such as vermiculite, rock wool, expanded clay, pumice, peat, coconut fibre, volcanic lapillus, sand, gravel.

The substrate must have the following characteristics

- maintain a constant water balance, retaining moisture, but also allowing excess water to drain off to prevent the development of root system diseases.
- offer support to the plant, without damaging the root system.

It follows that the best characteristics are given by a bottom (3-4 cm) of well-draining substrate (e.g. pumice or expanded clay), and then fill the container (up to a few cm from the upper edge), with a substrate with greater water retention from nursery (e.g. coconut fibre).

- The management of the vegetable garden involves the use of different tools and the following activities, to be carried out daily, weekly or monthly according to these guidelines:
- daily: check the water level in the collection tank, check the regular dripping from the sprinklers, and the drainage. If there is no dripping, unscrew the dripper to check for any fillings. In case of failure to drain and fill the water container, disconnect the drain microtube and check for any fillings from the substrate or roots of the plant.
- weekly: top up the water content in the collection tank and add 1-1.5 g/litre of fertilizer.
- monthly: transplant the new plants, taking care to remove the crop residues from the previous cycle and, if necessary, refill the containers with substrate.

Nicolas Campos

CHAPTER 3 - Types of Hydroponic Systems

Some of the best hydroponic systems on the market combine different types of hydroponics in a hydroponic hybrid system.

There are several techniques that you can use to get the nutrient solution for your plants.

Nutrient film technique

Nutrient Film Techinque, or NFT, is a type of hydroponic system in which a continuous flow of nutrient solution flows over plant roots. This type of solution makes use of inclined planes so that the nutrient solution will flow with the force of gravity.

This type of system works very well because the roots of a plant absorb more oxygen from the air than from the nutrient solution itself. Because only the root tips come into contact with the nutrient solution, the plant can get more oxygen which promotes a faster growth rate.

Deep water cultivation

Deepwater Culture (DWC), also known as the reservoir method, is by far the easiest method for growing plants with hydroponics. In a Deepwater Culture hydroponic system, the roots are suspended in a nutrient solution. An aquarium air pump oxygenates the nutrient solution.

Flow and reflux

A flow and reflow hydroponic system are an excellent system for growing plants with hydroponics. This type of system works by flooding the growing area with nutrient solution at specific intervals. The nutrient solution then slowly drains into the reservoir with an overflow. The pump is programmed by a timer, so the process is repeated at specific intervals so that your plants get the desired amount of nutrients.

A flow and reflow hydroponic system are ideal for plants that are used to dry periods. Some plants thrive when they go through a short dry period because it causes the root system to become larger in search of moisture. As the root system gets bigger, the plant grows faster because it can absorb more nutrients.

Aeroponics

Aeroponics is a hydroponic method whereby the roots are sprayed with a nutrient solution while suspended in the air. There are two main methods of getting the solution to the exposed roots. The first method involves a fine spray nozzle to spray the roots. The second method uses what is called a fogger, a nebulizer that saturates the environment with the nutrient solution.

Wicking

Wicking is one of the easiest and most convenient methods of hydroponics. The basic concept of cultivation is that you use a material, such as cotton, which is surrounded by growing soil with one end of the wick fed into the nutrient solution.

Perlite or vermiculite is usually used in this type of system. The use of substances such as rock wool, coconut fibre or peat is not recommended as they can absorb too much of the nutrient solution.

Drip system

A hydroponic drip system is quite simple. The system works by providing a slow supply of nutrient solution to the hydroponic medium. It is recommended to use a slow draining medium, such as rock wool, coconut fibre or peat moss.

The disadvantage of a system like this is that the drains can become clogged, so it requires continuous maintenance and control.

The 4 Best Hydroponic Cultivation Techniques

When designing a hydroponic crop, various factors have to be taken into account such as the type of plant (e.g. tomatoes, strawberries or salad), the place where it will be mounted (indoor growing or outdoor greenhouse), the size of the system or the environment.

All these factors influence the choice of the type of techniques to use and consequently we will show you the 4 best hydroponic growing techniques, among them none is the best but each one is perfect to use according to a specific situation. Which type of hydroponic growing technique to use in each situation is best suited to your needs.

Hydroponic Cultivation Technique in DWC

DWC, which stands for Deep Water Culture, is a hydroponic growing technique that consists of growing plants in a highly oxygenated solution based on water and fertilizers.

Compared to other hydroponic cultivation methods, which use an inert substrate such as expanded clay, rockwool, perlite etc. for propagation, the DWC is a technique of deep-water cultivation.

root, in DWC the roots are completely (or almost) immersed in the solution that will act as both substrate and carrier for nutrients.

It is therefore possible to grow large plants with a minimum use of substrate, all that is needed is a handful of expanded clay in which the young plant can take root and support it until the roots come out of the pot and are able to develop into the solution. For this reason, the cultivation in deep water can be considered a middle way between traditional hydroponics and aeroponics.

The advantages of growing in DWC can be summarised in:

- Accelerated growth, as the increased oxygen concentration at the roots stimulates nutrient uptake and plant metabolism
- Increased production: plants grown in DWC have higher yields than those grown on land
- Minimum use of substrate: it will no longer be necessary to move large volumes of soil or other substrates as only a minimum amount of expanded clay is needed to grow large plants.

- Low maintenance: there are no drip heads that could clog or water pumps that would block the irrigation of the plants in the event of a malfunction. Even in the event of a blackout, plants grown in DWC would survive

Deep water cultivation is best suited to those situations where the temperature can be controlled, the water temperature, which is why they lend themselves well to being used indoors for growing medium or large plants. On the other hand, they are less suitable in very hot places, unless a solution refrigeration system such as a chiller is used.

A variant of deep-water cultivation are the so-called floating systems, mainly used for the cultivation of salads, where the plants are placed on panels that float inside a tank. The roots grow immersed in the solution, which must be oxygenated by movement pumps or aerators.

NFT Hydroponic Cultivation Technique (Nutrient Film Tecnique)

It is based on the principle that the root of the plant grows and develops in contact with a continuously flowing veil of water, in this way it is continuously enriched by the gaseous exchange with the oxygen present in the air and the roots absorb the nutrients and oxygen present in the solution.

Usually these systems are composed of perforated conduits, connected to a storage tank and a pump that constantly keeps the solution in circulation. It is important that the pump always works, in the event of a shutdown the solution would cease to reach the roots which could dry out in a few hours.

Hydroponic Cultivation Technique Dutch Vessels

It is a plastic jar, with a square or rectangular base, with a shape that allows it to be arranged along a drain line leading to an accumulation tank. From this, through a pump, the solution is distributed from above to each pot, irrigates the roots and flows back through the drain channel.

In Dutch pots the roots of the plants grow inside clay or perlite, materials with a good draining power that let a lot of air and therefore oxygen pass through them. The plants receive the necessary water and nutrients through drip troughs. A symphonic element at the bottom of each pot ensures that there are always a few centimetres of solution available, which in the event of a blackout would act as a reserve, giving the grower more time to intervene.

Another big advantage is that they lend themselves to being individually mounted, you can vary the distance between them, they can be arranged on different levels or they can be moved easily from one place to another (for example indoors they can be moved from the vegetative room to the flowering room).

This system is quite easy to implement and lends itself very well to use in both domestic and commercial greenhouses.

Hydroponic Cultivation Technique on Coconut Plates

Coconut is a substrate with excellent characteristics for hydroponic cultivation, has good water retention, protects the root system and at the same time offers an excellent air passage and therefore better oxygenation.

Before it can be used for this purpose, the coconut fibre is washed and filtered, then dehydrated and compacted into blocks or slabs that make it convenient for storage. These must be rehydrated before they can be reused, at which point the fibre will absorb the water and increase in volume by up to 5 times.

Since it is an inert substrate, therefore free of nutrients, these will have to be supplied through a nutrient solution, which will be administered at time intervals through drippers with a series of daily cycles.

Another big advantage is the possibility to be reused and be able to grow for 2 or 3 cycles with the same substrate.

Coconut plates lend themselves to the cultivation of all plants and are particularly popular in strawberry crops. The slabs can be placed on overhead channels or supports that make it easy for the grower to work as well as harvest.

CHAPTER 4 - How to make a DIY Hydroponic Garden

If you are interested in the idea of a hydroponic garden, we recommend that you try to make your own hydroponic garden before you turn to expert hands. The operation is far from complicated and could be a great idea to spend some spring Sundays waiting for summer in a useful and fun way.

How to Prepare Environment and Material

Lighting

Indoor hydroponic cultivation should be in places with direct and continuous exposure to the sun, such as a balcony or terrace greenhouse. If you do not have such a place it may be necessary to provide additional lighting for your crop.

Hydroponic kits are usually sold with the necessary lamps, but if you have decided to create your own system by buying components individually you need to know which lights to take.

The best lighting for hydroponic crops is provided by High Intensity Discharge (HID) lamps, available in either metal halide (MH) or high-pressure sodium (HPS) versions. The latter emits a more orange light, very suitable for plants in the vegetative growth phase.

Another type of lighting used in hydroponic grow rooms is T5, which generates the typical fluorescent light, with high efficiency, low heat and low energy consumption. It is especially suitable for growing cuttings and plants with short growth cycles.

For higher yields, be sure to set a timer to turn the lamps on and off so that you always provide a regular dose of light to your indoor grow. Most edible plants require at least 6 hours of sunlight per day.

Room conditions

It is very important that hydroponics is installed in a room with the right conditions. Key elements include relative humidity, temperature, CO_2 levels and air circulation.

The ideal humidity for a hydroponic grow box is between 40-60% relative humidity. Higher humidity levels, especially in environments with poor air circulation, can cause powdery mildew formation and other problems to your crop.

If the climate requires it, it may be necessary to install a humidifier or dehumidifier to regulate the humidity in the room, always keeping it at an optimal level.

The right temperature for a crop is around 20-21 °C centigrade. If the temperatures are too high, excessively hot water could lead to root decomposition.

The perfect environment for home hydroponics should also have a large supply of carbon dioxide. The more CO_2 is available, the faster the plants will grow. The best way to do this is to make sure the room has a constant air flow.

Water quality

The choice of water influences the final yield of hydroponic cultivation. In terms of chemical composition all waters are different. Pay attention to two factors that influence the ability of the liquid to provide dissolved nutrients to plants: the level of mineral salts, measured in PPM, and the pH.

A "hard" water, with a high mineral content, is already more saturated and does not dissolve nutrients as effectively as water with a lower mineral concentration. If it has a high level of PPM, you can try filtering it to increase its capacity.

The ideal pH level is between 5.8 and 6.2. A hydroponic crop therefore prefers a slightly acidic environment: if your water does not reach this level you can use chemicals to adjust the pH in the ideal range.

Nutrients

The nutrients used in hydroponic crops are available in both liquid and dry form and in organic or synthetic form. However, all of them can be dissolved in water to create the nutrient compound useful for growth.

The product used should include the main macronutrients and micronutrients that a plant would find in the soil:

- nitrogen
- potassium
- phosphorus
- Football
- magnesium
- iron
- manganese
- boron
- zinc

- copper
- molybdenum
- chlorine

Avoid using standard garden fertilizers in a hydroponic crop: these are compounds designed for use in soil, not suitable for the concentrations required by hydroponics at home.

First Method

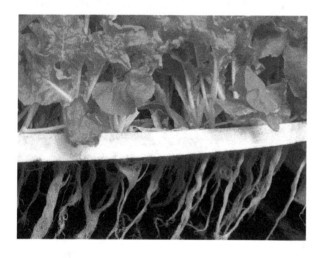

Tools Required

In principle, you will need them to create your hydroponic garden:

> ➤ a large, dark-coloured container to serve as a root tank, perhaps a disused aquarium (the sun's rays must not filter out, so if necessary, cover the container with black paint on the outside).

> ➤ hydroponics jars or plastic cups (better if recycled of course).

> ➤ polystyrene to cover the container as a lid and fix the supports for the seedlings.

> ➤ a breathable anchor substrate (perlite, vermiculite, expanded clay, depending on preference).

> ➤ an air pump to oxygenate the solution.

> ➤ porous stones on which to anchor the pump tube.

> ➤ nutrients for hydroponics.

Step-By-Step Instructions

Here is now the procedure for creating your own hydroponic garden:

> ➤ Start by drilling holes in the polystyrene panel so that you can insert the paper cups, taking care that the upper part of the future plant remains exposed to light. Also make a hole for the air pump tube.

➢ Then connect the air pump tube to the porous stone and place it on the bottom of the container.

➢ Now fill the tank with a solution based on water and hydroponic nutrients (which you can buy in common gardening shops), mixing according to the instructions on the packaging and placing the polystyrene lid over the structure.

➢ Finally, place the plastic cups or hydroponic pots, previously filled with a bit of anchor substrate, into the polystyrene support.

➢ Your hydroponic growing system is now ready for use. All you must do is plant the seeds and wait for your lush home garden to grow beautifully.

Remember to keep the air pump running to ensure good oxygenation and change the solution at least twice a month. If you have the impression that the aqueous solution has been significantly reduced, it may be appropriate to add more.

We advise you, in similar cases, to alternate simple water to compound solution, in order to avoid over-saturation of the plants and to enjoy economic savings.

An alternative, for those who do not have the time, the space or the intention to work so hard, may be to buy some bottles for hydroponic cultivation already ready for use. On the internet you will find various kinds of bottles.

These are, in general, nice and colourful bottles of recycled wine, properly filled with the necessary substances and planted with basil, parsley, oregano, mint and garlic.

Second Method

Hydroponics is a special technique where plants are grown above ground but in water, becoming their main habitat. But what are the steps to implement hydroponics?

Step 1 - Prepare well for hydroponic cultivation

Let's prepare the seeds

First take a kitchen glass or coffee cup and fill it with tap water and soak the seeds in it for 24 hours.

This promotes the hydration of the seed and activates the germination hormone as well as softening the cuticle (skin) of the seed and thus allowing better germination. The plant will have to use less force to break the shell (less stress) and you will get plants that are born very close to each other (homogeneity germination).

Let's prepare the Rockwool

We immerse the rockwool cubes in a container with water regulated at Ph 5.5 for 24h.

Contrary to what is believed this step is fundamental for two reasons:

It allows the water passing through the rockwoll to remain at the same pH and not to undergo variations that could raise or lower the entire pH of our tank (nutrient solution).

The seedling will grow from the first phase of life with the perfect pH value to fully assimilate all the nutrients of our solution.

Take a pH meter (electronic pH meter), calibrate it and adjust the pH of the water to 5.5. Then soak in as many cubes as you need for the number of plants you want to grow (3 rockwolls = 3 plants).

Let's prepare the clay

Now all that remains is to prepare the last fundamental component of our hydroponic system, clay. Take a large basin, fill it with water up to about half and pour a few drops of hydrogen peroxide to disinfect it.

Thanks to this step you will eliminate the sand in the middle of the clay, which could clog the hydroponic system and disinfect it from possible bacteria that could proliferate inside the water of the systems.

Take a pot from your hydroponic system and fill it to the brim with clay, pour the clay into the basin and repeat this step for the number of pots in your system (if my system has 10 pots I will repeat the operation 10 times).

This allows you to calculate the right amount of clay to fill all the vessels in your system, since we will have to calibrate and rinse it before inserting it into the system itself. Let's calibrate the water in the bowl at a pH of less than 4.5 and let it rest for 24h.

This allows the water that will pass in the future in the middle of the clay, not to undergo changes in ph, which could change the entire ph of the solution present in the tank.

The roots that will expand, wrapping all the clay, will find an environment with perfect ph to absorb all the nutrients of the system.

We take our clay after 24 hours and rinse it under running tap water, to eliminate all the residues present, we are ready to fill our pots!

Step 2 - Commissioning of the Hydroponic System

At this point we have everything you need to put our hydroponics plant into operation, ready to give you great satisfaction and above all heavy harvests! Follow these tips to get off to the top right away!

How much water in my system?

In all hydroponic systems the total capacity of the reservoir is indicated in the user manual, obviously that indicated is the maximum capacity, so we should insert less water than the one indicated in the booklet.

If you have a small hydroponics system (4-8 plants) please enter 10 litres less than the capacity indicated in the manual.

If you have a large hydroponic system (over 10 pots) insert 15 litres less than the maximum capacity.

At this point you also need to know that you must use a certain type of water to fill your system:

> ➢ 65% Tap water.
> ➢ 35% Osmotic water (distilled)

Otherwise you can fill the whole system with 100% Osmotic Water.

To fill the system, I mainly use 30l of water which I divide into 10 litres of osmotic water (which I get using my reverse osmosis filter) and 20 litres of tap water. The water must have a temperature between 18-24° for the roots to remain well oxygenated.

Before you put the water into your system read step 2 below.

Preparation of nutrients and ph

After we have filled a 20l tank with tap water and 10l osmotic water (if you use a system that holds 30l) before pouring the tanks into the system, we must adjust the amount of fertilizer and ph.

Following the diagram that indicates the recommended amount for each week of growth (expressed in ml) I know that I must pour 2.5 ml every 10 litres of water. I then calculate 2.5 x 3 = 7.5ml (since I have 30 litres in the tank) and then I feed the tanks before pouring them so that I can adjust the pH, before putting them into the hydroponic system.

To distribute the food in the 2 tanks I put 5ml in the 20l tank and 2.5ml in the 10l tank (2.5ml every 10 litres). Now I shake the cans to distribute the fertilizer evenly in the water and wait 2 minutes (the fertilizer lowers the pH of the water).

I measure the Ph with the Ph Tester and add Ph- until I get a value of 5.5 - 5.8. Now we can pour the tanks with the nutrients into the hydroponic system, every time we change the water to the system, we will use this system by putting the fertilizer first and adjusting the pH before pouring the solution.

Tip: It is always good practice to make a sign to indicate the water level when the system contains exactly the litres you have chosen to use so you can monitor when the water level starts to drop.

I will teach you what to do when the water level drops too low.

We time our system

We pour the water into the system and operate the pump, every time we change the water, we run the pump for at least an hour or so to distribute the new nutrients to our plants. Now we just must set the timer to time the pump operation and irrigation of the system.

There are 2 schemes to follow:

- Until the roots of the plants do not reach the water inside the tank (if you use a system similar to mine) we have to run the timer in 15 minute steps every hour (we lower 1 horsemen of the timer every hour, if you do not know how to program the timer watch my video: Programming a timer). We must maintain this programming even when our lamps are off or during the night period.
- The roots are immersed in the water of the system: we keep 15 minutes of irrigation every hour during the light period (lamps on) and we interrupt the programming during the night period. We will run 30 minutes of watering only halfway through the dark period so if our dark period lasts 6 hours we will run at 3 hours 30 minutes of watering, if we are in bloom where our dark period lasts instead 12 hours we will run the system after 6 hours of darkness for 30 minutes.

If the system you use is done differently and the roots of the plant do not touch the water in the reservoir, or run it 15 minutes every hour, both during the light and dark period.

Add hydroponic liquid fertilizer weekly

Empty the system completely every 3 weeks.

Follow this program:

Week 1 pay the amount corresponding to the week your plants have and fill the system with the chosen litres (30l in my case).

2nd Week do not change the water in your system completely but add the fertilizers that are indicated for the week corresponding to your growing cycle.

Remember to add distilled water to bring the system back to the litres you have chosen (if you mark the water level on the system with a marker pen, when you have just added the litres you have chosen to use, you can see visually how much water you need to add to bring the system back to the right capacity).

Always use distilled osmotic water to top up the system.

3rd Week add the fertilizers corresponding to the week you are in without changing the water completely topped up to bring the system back to the right level.

Start 4th Week completely empty the system by draining all the water in the system via pump or drain hose. Fill the system back up to the present level and add fertilizer to the week you are in.

Constant monitoring of our hydroponic system

Finally, the last step to follow, is to constantly monitor our hydroponic system(s) daily in order to get the most out of our seedlings.

Hydroponics, unlike growing in soil, is much more sensitive to pH changes and could change as it rises or falls, even in a short period of time, so experienced growers use pH-meters on the monitor to always see what pH the solution is at and can intervene to change the parameter as soon as possible.

I recommend keeping the pH as close to 5.5 and 5.6 as possible as this is the absolute best range to fully absorb all nutrients.

So, remember to check the pH of your system every day and adjust it with ph+ or ph- products to bring your value back to the perfect parameter.

If possible, rotate the pots in your system daily or rotate the whole system to distribute the light in the best way for your plants.

If you are a first time user, we recommend that you follow the doses shown on the fertiliser scheme to avoid excesses or nutrient defects, the important thing is to set the pH to fully absorb the fertiliser and not add it randomly creating imbalances.

Nicolas Campos

CHAPTER 5 - Plants for Hydroponic Gardening

In principle, all plants can be grown with the hydroponic system, except for some bulb plants and fat plants that prefer dry soil and dry air.

What is more evident is that many plants benefit from this cultivation technique and develop more luxuriantly, thanks to the constant supply of nutrients and the absence of pathogens or pests.

As far as garden or ornamental plants are concerned, green leafy species find in the hydroponic greenhouse an ideal environment to grow and develop luxuriantly: ficus, pothos, dracena, philodendron and others similar.

Among the flowering plants, anthurium, spathiphyllum, spathiphyllum, saintpaulia and the like easily adapt to the hydroponic system and give rich and colourful inflorescences.

Finally, a special mention should be made of the orchids which, when grown above ground in a hydroponic greenhouse, find a perfect environment for growing vigorous and luxuriant.

Hydroponic cultivation, then, as mentioned, offers great satisfaction and potential in the cultivation of vegetables and aromatic plants.

Even at home you can benefit from the positive aspects that a small domestic vegetable garden can give to the whole family. Vegetables and vegetables, in fact, fed with the right fertilizers, grow and develop without limits of seasonality, giving genuine and excellent quality fruit throughout the year.

The vegetables and vegetables that give the best results in hydroponics are:

- tomatoes.
- peppers.
- cucumbers.
- all green leafy vegetables (chard, mustard, salads, lettuce, rocket and so on).

Also, aromatic herbs, such as basil, sage, chives and others, give excellent results with abundant production and can be used to flavour and give fragrance to all foods in the kitchen.

To get the most out of the small domestic vegetable garden it is advisable to grow vegetables with similar needs. For this reason, it is better to get information and documentation in order to guarantee a quantity of harvest that meets your needs without wasting time and energy.

Regarding the substrate, it is advisable to use a mixture of expanded clay and coconut fibre.

Irrigation is important because it helps to keep the moisture content of the substrate constant and, above all, it is the main vehicle for the administration of fertilizer for plant growth.

The most suitable nutrient solution should be chosen according to the type of plant and its vegetative period, depending on whether it is in the germination or production phase.

In the cultivation of the vegetable garden, then, it is essential to control the pH of the substrate whose value must always be within certain limits to avoid damaging the roots and the plants themselves. On the market you can find suitable instruments for this purpose for measuring the pH of the substrate or alternatively you can use cheaper litmus paper.

CHAPTER 6 - How to Grow

How to Grow Tomatoes with Hydroponics

Tomatoes obtained by hydroponic cultivation grow in a nutrient solution instead of being planted directly into the soil, although they are usually attached to a non-soil substrate that can support their roots and is capable of releasing nutrients. Growing tomatoes by this method allows the grower to grow them in a controlled environment, with less risk of disease, ensures faster development and higher fruit yield. However, this technique requires more effort and sometimes more money than traditional cultivation, especially if you have never built or started a hydroponics plant before.

Tools needed:

> Large plastic container
> PVC Pipes
> Plastic "flow and reflux" tray
> Water pump
> Grow lamps, e.g. metal halide lights (recommended)
> Two motorized timers (one for the pump, one for the lighting)
> Tomato seeds
> Rock wool
> Mesh vessels or other vessels that allow water drainage
> Nutrient solution
> pH test kit
> Potassium hydroxide (or other substance that reduces the pH)

- Phosphoric acid (or other substance that raises the pH)
- Thermostat
- Fan
- Brush
- Poles and clips or laces

Creating a Hydroponic Growing Plant

Determine which system you want to use. There are different types of hydroponic systems, tomatoes can grow well in all of them. This tutorial provides instructions on how to build an ebb and flow system, which is relatively inexpensive and easy to set up. However, you can also look for alternatives, such as the simpler 'water growing' system suitable for cherry tomatoes and other small plants, or the more complex 'multi Flow' or 'NFT' systems, which are usually used by farms.

Find a suitable site. Hydroponics systems are only suitable for indoor environments or greenhouses. They must be carefully controlled to function properly, so they must be installed in some area isolated from other rooms or from outside. This allows the temperature and humidity to be set to precise levels, which is essential to achieve the best growth.

You can grow with the hydroponic method using natural light, while keeping the plant under a glass or polyethylene cover to create a greenhouse effect, not open to the air.

Fill a large plastic container with water to use as a reservoir. Take one that does not let light through, to prevent algae growth. The larger this tank is, the more stable the plant will be, providing a better chance of success. At a minimum, small tomato plants (like Pachino's tomatoes) require 1.9 litres of water, while most slightly larger tomato plants need 3.8 litres each. However, there can be many factors that lead plants to use water more quickly, so it is a good idea to get a container with twice the minimum amount needed.

You can get a bucket or plastic basket for this purpose. Use a new one to avoid any possible contamination of the plant or, at least, one that is only partially used, if it is thoroughly washed with soap and water and rinsed beforehand.

For this type of crop, collected rainwater may be more suitable than tap water, especially if the latter is particularly "hard" with a high mineral content.

Place a tray on top of the tank and secure it properly. This "ebb and flow" tray is intended to support tomato plants and should be periodically flooded with water and nutrients so that the roots of the plants can absorb them. It should be solid enough to support the plants (or be placed on top of an additional reinforcement) and placed over the reservoir to allow excess water to flow down. The tray is usually made of plastic, not metal, to avoid possible corrosion that could damage the plants and wear out the tray.

Install a water pump inside the tank. You can buy one in a specialist hydroponics store or use a fountain pump that you can find in DIY stores. Many pumps have indications for water flow at different heights. You can use these diagrams to find a pump powerful enough to send water from the tank to the tray containing the plants. The best thing, however, would be to get yourself a powerful adjustable pump and try different settings once you have installed the system.

Install the filling tube between the tank and the tray. Take a 1.25 cm PVC hose, or the type of hose you find in the hydroponics kit, and attach one end of it between the water pump and the tray, so that the tray can be flooded to the height of the plant's roots.

Install an overflow fitting that leads to the tank. Connect a second piece of PVC pipe to the tray with an overflow element, positioned at the height of the top of the roots, slightly below where the stems will sprout. When the water reaches this level, it is discharged through this pipe into the tank.

Connect a timer to the water pump. You can use a simple timer of those suitable for lamps to power the water pump at regular intervals. This should be adjustable so that you can increase or decrease the amount of nutrients depending on the stage of plant development.

You should use a robust 15 ampere timer with a waterproof cover.

Each water pump should have a way to connect a timer if it doesn't already have one, but the exact instructions vary depending on the model. Ask the manufacturer or the store if you have any problems installing it.

Test the system. Turn on the water pump and check where it flows. If the water flow cannot reach the tray or overflows from the edges, you may need to adjust the pump settings. Once the water force is set correctly, check the timer to see if the pump is on schedule.

Growing Tomatoes

Bury the seeds in a specific material. When possible, try to start cultivation from the seed. If you take the plants directly from the outside soil, you risk introducing pests and diseases into the hydroponic system. Take the seeds from the plant and buy them from the nurseries, already prepared in trays containing a specific substrate for hydroponics, instead of normal soil. Usually 2,5 cm3 of material called "rock wool" is the most common choice, such as lava stone or long filaments of coconut fibre. Before using it, soak the material in water with a pH of

4,5. Plant the seed under the surface, hold the tray under the plastic dome or other transparent material to trap moisture and encourage the seeds to germinate.

In garden shops you can find kits to test the pH of the soil or material, as well as the acidity of the water, as well as some materials or kits that can change or adjust the pH.

Bury the seeds in a specific material. When possible, try to start growing from the seed. If you take the plants directly from outside soil, you risk introducing pests and diseases into the hydroponic system. Take the seeds from the plant and buy them from the nurseries, already prepared in trays containing a specific substrate for hydroponics, instead of normal soil. Usually 2,5 cm3 of material called "rock wool" is the most common choice, such as lava stone or long filaments of coconut fibre. Before using it, soak the material in water with a pH of 4,5. Plant the seed under the surface, hold the tray under the plastic dome or other transparent material to trap moisture and encourage the seeds to germinate.

In garden shops you can find kits to test the pH of the soil or material, as well as the acidity of the water, as well as some materials or kits that can change or adjust the pH.

When they germinate, put the seedlings under artificial light. As soon as they sprout, remove the cover and place the seedlings under a light source for at least 12 hours a day. Use incandescent bulbs only as a last resort, as they produce more heat than other solutions.

Read the next section for more details about the lighting system.

Be careful not to leave the light directly on the roots to avoid damaging them. If the roots protrude from the seedbed before they are ready to be transplanted, you may need to add more material to cover them.

Transfer the seedlings to the hydroponic plant. Wait until the roots start to protrude from the bottom of the tray and the first 'real leaf', which is larger and looks different from the first two 'seed leaves', has grown. This usually takes a period of 10-14 days. When you move the seedlings in the hydroponic growing system, you can distance them 15 cm from each other, placing them in a layer of the same material or transferring them in single plastic "jars" provided they always have the same growing substratum.

If you follow the flow and reflow method described in this article, the plants are placed on the tray. Other systems may involve placing the plants in a tray, along a slope, or anywhere else where water and nutrients can reach the roots.

Set the water pump timer. At the beginning, set the pump so that the water flows for 15 or 30 minutes four times a day (once every six hours). Keep an eye on the plants: you need to increase the frequency of watering if they start to wilt and reduce it if the roots become slimy or become excessively soaked. Ideally, the material the plants are in should be slightly dry before the next watering cycle is activated.

Even if you set the irrigation scheduling correctly, it may be necessary to increase the frequency of irrigation when the plants begin to bloom and bear fruit, as these processes require more water.

Set artificial lights (if provided). To have ideal growing conditions, plants should be exposed to light between 16 and 18 hours every day. After that, the lights should be turned off and the plants kept in total darkness for about 8 hours. Plants can grow if you rely on sunlight, but probably grow more slowly.

Place poles and prune the plants on the tops. Some tomato plants are "determined" growing, in the sense that they grow to a specific size, then stop. Others continue to grow indefinitely, and you may need to gently tie them to a pole to make them grow straight. If you must prune them, break the stems with your hands rather than cutting them.

Pollinate the flowers of the plants. When the tomatoes bloom, since there are no insects in the hydroponic plant environment that can pollinate them, you'll have to do it yourself. Wait until the petals bend and expose the round pistil and cover the stamens, the long thin sticks in the centre of the flower, with pollen. Touch each pollen-covered stamen with a soft brush, then touch the rounded end of the pistil. Repeat this process every day.

System Setting

Check the temperature. During "daytime" hours it must be 18 - 24°C. At night it should be between 12 and 18°C. Use a thermostat and fans to regulate the temperature. Keep it monitored during plant growth, as it may change with the climate or the life cycle of the tomatoes.

Turn on a fan in the room. An outward facing fan or another room can help maintain the correct temperature throughout the room. The airflow it creates can also make pollination easier, although to make sure it does, you should pollinate by hand anyway, as described earlier.

Add a nutrient solution into the water tank. Choose a specific nutrient solution for hydroponic crops, not a normal fertilizer. Avoid 'organic' solutions, as they can decompose and make growing more complex. Because planting needs differ depending on the variety of tomato and minerals in the water, you may need to adjust the amount or type of nutrient solution you use. To get started, however, follow the instructions on the packaging to determine how much product you need to add to the tank.

Solutions with two nutrient components create less waste and can be adjusted in case of problems, as they can be mixed in different proportions, which makes them preferable to those composed of only one element.

You can use a concentrated formula during the growing phase of the plants and switch to a more specific formula for flowering, when the plant flowers, to meet these new nutritional requirements.

Use a kit to test the pH of the water and adjust the water level. You can use one of these commercially available kits or a litmus paper to test the pH of the nutrient and water mixture once you have had time to create a homogeneous compound. If the pH is outside the range of 5.8 to 6.3, ask a salesman in a hydroponics shop or garden centre for materials you can use to reduce or raise the pH.

Phosphoric acid is generally used to lower the pH, while potassium hydroxide is good for raising it.

Install grow lamps. Artificial "grow lights" allow you to simulate ideal growing conditions all year round, giving your tomatoes many more hours of "sunshine" than they could get in the garden. This is one of the main advantages of an indoor growing system. However, if you are growing in a greenhouse or other area that receives large amounts of natural light, you can settle for a shorter growing season and save on electricity bills.

Metal halide lamps (HQI) simulate sunlight more accurately, so they are the most popular choice for hydroponic growing systems. You can also find fluorescent, sodium and LED lamps on the market, but they cause slower growth or affect the shape of plants. Avoid incandescent bulbs because they are inefficient and short-lived compared to other options.

Constantly check the water. An electrical conductivity meter, or "conductivity meter", can be expensive, but it is the best way to measure the concentration of nutrients in water. If you find results outside the range of 2.0-3.5, it means that the water must be changed totally or partially. If you do not have this instrument, look for the following signs in your plants:

The leaf tips curling down may mean that the solution is too concentrated. Dilute with water from pH 6.0.

Leaf tips curling upwards or a red stem indicates a pH too low, while yellow leaves indicate that the pH is too high, or the solution is too diluted. In these cases, change the solution as described below.

Change the water and nutrient solution regularly. If the water level in the tank drops, add more water, but do not add more nutrients. Every two weeks, or once a week if the plants don't look healthy, empty the reservoir completely and rinse the support material and roots of the plants with natural pH 6.0 water to filter out and clean up any build-up of minerals that could cause damage. Fill the reservoir with a new solution of water and nutrients, taking care to balance the pH and let the mixture amalgamate before starting the pump.

You can use the water you used for rinsing to water your garden plants normally.

How to Grow Strawberries with the Hydroponic Method

Tools needed

> ➤ Strawberry seedlings
> ➤ Nutrient mix for hydroponic cultivation
> ➤ 20 l plastic container
> ➤ Bucket
> ➤ Vermiculite
> ➤ Waterproof sheet (optional)
> ➤ Spray bottle

Buy a strawberry plant and a nutrient mixture for hydroponically grown plants from a local nursery (hydroponically grown plants need a special mixture of mineral salts so that they can receive enough nutrients to grow properly).

Buy a 20-l plastic food container with drainage holes in the bottom.

Fill about 2/3 of the container with vermiculite.

Wet the vermiculite thoroughly with water to moisturize it. This will prevent the roots of the strawberries from drying out when you need to transplant them.

Choose a well-lit and tempered spot to place the container. Strawberries grown using the hydroponic method need a temperature that oscillates between 14 and 21°C.

Fill a bucket with cold water.

Carefully remove a strawberry seedling from its container. Remove the soil attached to the roots by shaking them gently. You can also give a few light strokes with your fingers to make it fall.

Soak the whole root system in the bucket water for at least 10 minutes.

Lift the roots out of the bucket and rinse them under a light jet of cold running water to make sure you remove all the soil.

Remove any dry, brittle or dead leaves.

Place the seedling carefully in the pot. Hold the plant by the collar and arrange the roots so that they lie on the vermiculite.

Add more vermiculite in the container to cover the roots, but not the collar; it should receive light and air.

Place the strawberry container in a sunny or well-lit spot.

Place a waterproof material under the container, such as some plastic sheeting, to protect the surface on which you will place the tray containing the strawberries.

Mix the nutrients for hydroponic growing with the water, following the instructions on the package.

Water the strawberries thoroughly with this nutrient solution.

Check the water level every day and, if necessary, add it so that the roots are always moist.

Tips

Strawberries, unlike other fruits, can continue to ripen after they have been picked. Therefore, do not pick them until they are fully ripe. In this case, they will be red and a little compact to the touch.

You need to give the strawberries a lot of light. If you do not have a window exposed to the sun, you should put the container under a progressive light.

Spray the strawberries with water using a spray bottle to increase moisture levels. These fruits grow better in a very humid environment, which also discourages parasites from attacking the leaves.

Warnings

Temperature is also a very important factor. If it is too high, the strawberries slow down or stop flowering and fruit production. If it is too low, they do not grow at all.

Take the utmost care when rinsing the soil from the roots. If you break too many root hairs, the plant will no longer produce fruit.

Other Methods for Hydroponic Strawberry Growing

Nutrient Film Technique (NFT) is a system in which the roots of plants are suspended on a film of nutrient solution. It is commonly used in large commercial systems.

Flow and drainage: nutrients are fed into the tray containing the strawberries. This container contains holes that allow the nutrient solution to recirculate, which goes to spray the roots of the plants.

How to Grow Vegetable Lettuce with the Hydroponic Method

Lettuce is the easiest vegetable to grow using the hydroponic method. Instead of growing lettuce in the soil, water, mineral salts, and another growth medium, such as gravel, are used. After setting up your hydroponic system, you'll have your first lettuce crop in a few weeks. This vegetable grows so fast, using the hydroponic method, that you can have lettuce grown at home all year round.

Tools Need

- ✓ Lettuce seeds or seedlings
- ✓ Bucket or another container
- ✓ Growth medium (gravel, sawdust, vermiculite, etc.).
- ✓ Water
- ✓ Nutrient salts
- ✓ Spoon (for mixing nutrients).

Choose a bucket or jar that has drainage holes at the bottom. The size of the container should be between 4.5 litres and 22.5 litres approximately.

Buy a pack with a nutrient mixture for hydroponic crops from your local nursery or home and garden shop. Don't skip this step: all plants developed with the hydroponic method must receive special nutrients.

Decide which type of growth medium you want to use. Gravel is the most convenient, but if you use gravel, you will need to water much more frequently. Other common choices include:

- ✓ Sand
- ✓ Shavings
- ✓ Sawdust
- ✓ Vermiculite

Fill the container with the growth medium of your choice. For best results, use an opaque container; excess light will promote algae growth in the water.

Measure your pre-mixed nutrients according to the instructions on the package and add the amount of water needed for your chosen container.

Mix the nutrient mixture into the water until it is completely dissolved. If you don't use the solution right away, mix again before you put the lettuce seeds or seedlings in it.

Put the lettuce seedlings or seeds into your solution. You will need 8-10 seeds or 3-4 seedlings for a small container.

Tips

If you don't have an opaque container, you can cover what you have with black plastic or aluminium foil to protect it from sunlight.

If you grow your lettuce outdoors in an indoor yard or terrace, be sure to protect it from the rain so that excess rainwater doesn't get into the container and dilute the nutrients.

Check the water level every day; the lettuce will not grow if the roots do not absorb water.

Warnings

If you grow lettuce indoors or outdoors, you need to worry about insects, and remove them from the leaves.

Aphids are the most common indoor pests, but if your lettuce container is outdoors, make sure you protect yourself from grasshoppers, snails and caterpillars.

Don't forget that hydroponic lettuce, or any plant grown without soil, still needs the support of a growth medium in addition to water.

Lettuce grown in this way needs between 15 and 18 hours of light every day. If you grow the lettuce indoors, you can place the container under a fluorescent lamp.

If you want to grow hydroponic lettuce in a suspended container or on a windowsill, be sure to choose a light growing medium, such as vermiculite, so that the container isn't too heavy.

Plants growing in a hydroponic environment require the support of water and nutrients, just like plants growing in soil.

How to Grow Aromatic Herbs in Hydroponics

There are many advantages of the hydroponic greenhouse: from the possibility to have always green and healthy plants, to the possibility to grow small vegetables and aromatic herbs without limits of seasonality. The management of a mini hydroponic greenhouse, then, is simple and cheap: just know the principles of its operation and the results will be evident.

Thanks to hydroponic cultivation, it is possible to create a small perfumed corner with aromatic plants and herbs, without having the encumbrance of pots and saucers.

Thanks to the method of water cultivation and LED light, the plants have what it takes to grow well and healthy, giving you a lot of satisfaction and making your indoor space cheerful and positive.

The mini greenhouse, in fact, is ideal for the cultivation of a large variety of plants in common use, also useful for those who love healthy cooking and a green lifestyle as close to nature as possible. The kit for hydroponic cultivation, then, is a perfect and versatile system to have at hand the herbs and aromatic plants you prefer.

There are no restrictions: in principle, all aromatic plants can be grown indoors using the hydroponic system. All you need to do is design your own greenhouse to keep the seedling cycle vital: from sowing in the substrate with the necessary nutrients, to lighting and the right temperature for the plants to grow.

So, if you decide to create a hydroponic greenhouse with a varied cultivation of seedlings, the advice is to select similar types that can live together: basil, parsley, mint, sage, and so on.

Hydroponics is well suited to the cultivation of aromatic plants and medicinal herbs, excellent natural remedies to alleviate seasonal ailments, help our metabolism and relax during winter days.

Each type of medicinal plant has different active ingredients and can therefore be taken according to personal needs. With indoor hydroponic cultivation it is possible to have some leaves available every day for an herbal tea or a good organic decoction.

The officinal herbs can be planted by sowing in a special rockwool substrate, or for such a plant, i.e. by stimulating the branching of some branches (cuttings) from the mother plant.

Once the seeds have sprouted, or the cuttings have released their roots, the aromatic and medicinal plants, with the help of natural fertilisers, will begin to develop luxuriantly and quickly before your eyes.

In hydroponic cultivation, the temperature and humidity level of the system must be kept under control: an alteration of these two parameters, in fact, can cause the onset of fungi and abnormalities in the plants. However, keeping the harmony of the small ecosystem under control is a simple operation that will gradually become natural and intuitive.

CHAPTER 7 - Prevention and Troubleshooting

Pest Prevention in Indoor Crops

Pest attack is one of the most frequent causes of crop failure, both in soil and in hydroponic systems. Very often it is more difficult to manage nutritional deficiencies.

Prevention is the best way to deal with plant pest infestations.

What do we mean by prevention? We mean essentially cleaning up and restricting access to unwanted organisms, the basic rules are:

Avoid having debris and plant matter on the floor (soil, dust, leaves etc.).

Always keep your tools clean (scissors, containers, pH-meters and conductive meters).

Avoid as much as possible that living organisms (insects, humans, etc.) have access to the grow box where you are growing. Install a filter that prevents the ventilation system from letting insects in with the air and control access and cracks.

It is a good rule to use clothes that you only wear when entering the grow room, the same for shoes. Pets are of course banned from the grow room.

Before putting a new plant in a grow box where there are other uninfected plants, leave it isolated for a few days and see if it shows signs of pests and diseases. Once it has passed the test it can be inserted together with the others.

Thanks to these measures you will be able to greatly reduce the risk of pests on your plants, but you can never be sure that they will not attack.

Possible infestations include:

insects: which attack foliage and stems and rarely the roots (root aphids).

Mushrooms: They can develop on both leaves and stems but become very dangerous when they attack the roots.

Nematodes: small vermiform organisms that attack the roots. Some varieties are beneficial.

Mites: Tetranichidi or "spiders" are among the most formidable in indoor crops.

Viruses: this is the worst thing that can happen to your plants in the grow box. These microorganisms start by deforming the leaves and then whole plants until they slowly kill them. Unfortunately, there is no cure and when a plant contracts a virus the crop is lost.

How to Recognize and Fight Plant Pests

In indoor cultivation we will find two main problems: insects and fungi. The best prevention measure against any infestation of insects and/or moulds and other microorganisms, is the cleaning - which must always be accurate and regular - of environments, pots, soil, tools and the farmer himself and his clothes (it is easy to bring with you microorganisms or insect larvae from outside).

A good and continuous ventilation of the rooms will also be essential, with a humidity rate that does not exceed 60% (especially during flowering) and a temperature that is not excessively high: these conditions are achieved with the use of an oscillating fan, which keeps the air in circulation and a correct internal air treatment that allows the continuous exchange.

In outdoor cultivation we will find the same problems as in indoor cultivation but attacks from snails, slugs and soil insects in general are more frequent.

Parasitic Root Mushrooms

Usually the roots are not given due attention. This statement is true whatever cultivation method is chosen, but even more so for hydroponic cultivation, since roots are sterile and vulnerable. Therefore, when choosing hydroponic cultivation, root care is extremely important.

But don't the roots take care of themselves? Usually they do, but only not at some point. If they find themselves in adverse situations, they are easy prey to various diseases. A good grower must prevent the problem before it occurs. The question is how to keep the root system healthy and healthy.

In hydroponic growing the main successful ingredients are a dynamic and well-designed growing system; clean and highly oxygenated water; a well-watered substrate; good ventilation and adequate temperature and humidity levels. Of course, there are many other parameters to consider but if you follow these basic guidelines and the usage tables on the nutrient bottles you will keep your plants happy and healthy. And at the end of the day this is exactly what you want, because insects and diseases start to invade a plant when it is stressed.

The root is a particularly vulnerable part of the plant, whether it is grown in soil or water. If the temperature is high and the water circulation is poor, your plants suffer from a lack of oxygen. At root level, this lack of oxygen reduces the permeability of the roots to water and consequently also the absorption of mineral salts, which leads to a weakening of the plant and, finally, to a poor harvest. If the plant is subjected to persistent stress conditions, the roots produce ethylene, a stress hormone that accumulates in the roots and participates in the slow degradation of the root system. In addition, some pathogens recognise ethylene as a sign of plant weakness and a reason to attack.

What is a pathogen?

It is an organism that causes a disease. In our environment there is an immense variety of pathogens, some of which are fungi such as Fusarium, Pythium, Verticillium, Phytophtora and many others. Fusarium and Pythium are the most destructive and common root attackers known both to hydroponic growers and to those who grow in the soil. These very ferocious invaders are often the cause of the destruction of a crop.

What is Pythium?

Pythium is a destructive root fungus parasite. Under suitable conditions, Pythium multiplies very quickly and releases microscopic spores that infect the root and deprive the plant of its nutrients. It attacks mainly seeds and seedlings, which offer less resistance to disease. Larger plants are more resistant, but they can still be attacked, with the difference that if the pathogen is detected quickly, they can be cured and saved, even if your crop is still scarce. Like other fungi, Pythium is present in any part of the plant and attacks practically all varieties Ì. The best conditions for its development are high humidity levels and a temperature between 20 and 30 degrees Celsius, as well as poor oxygenation of nutrients in case of hydroponic cultivation. It is a fungal spore that lives in air and water and is present in the growing area, even if you keep it clean. It climbs on your shoes, your clothes, your hands, etc. It ends up in your water, especially when it comes from wells, rivers or currents. There are millions of opportunities for this fungus to enter your garden. Therefore, it is important to keep your growing environment clean and try to understand where the water you use comes from.

Pythium is often identified as a "secondary infection" since it attacks the plant only when it has already started to suffer damage or when the growing conditions are not the best. It takes advantage of sick or injured tissues to colonize the root and create dripping or root rot.

How to recognize a Pythium attack?

In principle, when Pythium attacks, the infected seeds become soft, soft and black, after which they die. The stems of the seedlings become weak and weaken. Larger plants and mothers begin to wither and turn yellow for no apparent reason (therefore the process is mistakenly called nutritional deficiency) and sometimes the leaves tend to bend downwards. The plants show poor growth and the harvest is reduced. A total loss of harvest can also occur.

It is not easy to intercept an attack from Pythium in time, especially if you grow in soil, because it is difficult to see the first signs of stress on the surface. Only after a few days you notice that the plant looks sad. Meanwhile, at root level, the process has already started a long time ago. In hydroponics, Pythium, which loves and thrives in water, is a quite common disease.

If you are not vigilant enough, the consequences can be disastrous. However, hydroponics brings a new dimension to cultivation and offers the grower an invaluable advantage, namely access to the root system. In order to have better control over the future harvest, a good hydroponic grower must regularly inspect the root system, as roots say a lot about plant health, nutrient quality and the proper functioning of the cultivation system.

If you look at the roots when the Pythium has already started attacking your plants, you will notice different symptoms depending on the extent of the damage. The infection starts at the end of the root and then slowly disintegrates the root and lateral roots, which are very important for the absorption of nutrients. The bright white of the roots first turns light brown, then dark brown and finally black. When the infection is acute, the lower part of the stem can become slimy and black. Generally, it is possible to separate the rotten part of the root, which goes from soft to slimy, from the inner part.

How to fight Pythium?

The answer is quite simple: by keeping your plants healthy, you will allow them to resist fungal attacks. In hydroponic cultivation, there are some basic and obligatory rules to keep your plants healthy: good quality water, excellent oxygenation of the nutritive solution, good ventilation, a well sprayed substrate, adequate temperature and humidity levels, suitable nutrition programs and general cleanliness. These are the essential preventive measures that all hydroponics growers should always keep in mind, since prevention is the most effective weapon.

However, there are times when your plants are more vulnerable and that is when you should pay more attention to them.

1. Check the seedlings and cuttings closely, because it is usually at this stage that plants are attacked. It is important to choose the germination substrate very carefully and keep the germination area as clean as possible.

2. When preparing cuttings for propagation, use clean tools and take good care of both cuttings and mother plants, because the cuttings cut during propagation are an excellent opportunity' for pathogenic penetration.

3. As for the mother plant, when some stems are cut off, another phenomenon occurs: the root mass becomes too large for the new needs of the plant and therefore some parts start to deteriorate. At this point, the plant releases a greater quantity of ethylene and many pathogens, including Pythium, throw themselves headlong into it.

4. Do not hesitate to renew your mother plants. After a while, the mother plant becomes old and most likely carries Pythium spores. And the cuttings will obviously be full of them too. For this reason, it is advisable to use the mother plant two or three times and then replace it with one of the new rooted cuttings. In this way, you will always reproduce young, healthy mother plants and get healthy, vigorous, disease-free cuttings.

5. Transplanting is another key operation, since a wounded root is the ideal environment for an infection. Therefore, when transplanting, always use clean locations and be especially kind to young roots. To prevent the plant from transplanting stress and not to overhandle the roots, you can use aero-hydroponic propagation systems, especially when it comes to simply moving your plants from one pot to another so as not to interfere with the root system.

6. In principle, start with disease-free plants and seeds. Avoid over-feeding and overcrowding and maintain good ventilation. It seems that Pythium thrives better in the presence of high alkalinity levels Ì so try to keep the pH of your plants as low as possible while always trying to satisfy the plant's needs.

There are other methods to prevent Pythium and other fungi in general. Some companies offer products such as special silicate powders, bacteria or fungi, or mixtures of various species of both to add to your nutritive solution. Others go even further and offer a "bacterial filter" that filters out all residues, increases water oxygenation and includes a mixture of microorganisms that, once colonized, form a protective barrier on the roots, thus blocking the invasion of pathogenic organisms. For this filter to work well it is necessary to keep the roots healthy, even if you cannot control the temperature levels.

Administration of Nutrients or Fertilizers for Hydroponics

Indoor or nutrient fertilizers are available in different forms and types. It is important to make sure that the nutrient solution you use is suitable for the type of crop used (soil, hydroponics and aeroponics, coconut fibre). Fertilizers that have been designed and studied specifically for soil are only suitable for soil and not for hydroponics or coconut cultivation. One of the main reasons is that several trace elements are already present in the soil and therefore have not been added to the solution or fertilizer.

The true hydroponic nutrient solution must be complete, containing all the elements necessary for plant growth in its most soluble form. For this reason, hydroponic solutions tend to be more expensive. Trying to save on nutrients can lead to serious problems. Always try to use the best possible nutritional quality solutions, especially in hydroponics or aeroponics.

Fertilizing in Hydroponics and Aeroponics

The biggest advantage of hydroponic growth is that it allows you to precisely control the surrounding growing environment of your plants. This includes complete control of all available nutrients for the plant's roots. Soil growth does not allow such flexibility, as the soil can contain many minerals and salts. In a hydroponic system, the growing medium contains no nutrients per se, allowing the grower to control the exact amount of nutrients fed to their plant by adjusting the concentration of the hydroponic nutrient solution.

There are 3 main hydroponic nutrients that are required by your plants for maximum yield. These are Nitrogen (N), Phosphorus (P) and Potassium (K). The

114

concentration of each type is listed on the nutrient solution label. For example, a solution with 20-20-20 on the label contains 20% N, P 20% and 20% K. There are also many secondary hydroponic nutrients that are used by the plant at different times during its growth and flowering cycle but are not essential as primary nutrients. Small amounts of these minerals are added to hydroponic nutrients to ensure that your plants receive the full range of elements they need. Some of these secondary hydroponic nutrients include calcium, magnesium, sulphur, iron, molybdenum and boron.

Nicolas Campos

CHAPTER 8 - Maintenance of a Hydroponic Tank

Here is some practical and fundamental information to take care of the maintenance of your hydroponic tank. The reservoir is the fundamental part of any hydroponic growing system. These basics apply to any kind of system. Become a successful hydroponic grower by effectively maintaining your hydroponic reservoir.

Step-by-Step

This information applies to most vegetables that can be grown for human consumption.

Tools:

- pH meter
- PPM/TDS/EC sensor
- An aquarium air pump.
- Fertilizers for hydroponic systems
- Water
- Products for acidity alteration (pH+, pH-)

Every vegetable needs a specific amount of nutrients and acidity. There are guides that can be found online or in shops specialising in the sale of plant nutrients.

Check the water quality on a small sample with the fixed residue meter in parts per million (TDS/PPM) and electrical conductivity meter (EC) before inserting it into the tank. If the tap water measures 300 PPM or more, you will need to pass it through a reverse osmosis system or distil it. You must ensure that the parts per million of water are between 0-50 ppm, BEFORE inserting nutrients. Even if it's around 100 ppm, just pay attention to the micronutrients found in the tested water. See the "Tips" section for ideas on using tap water.

Use a digital probe to measure the hardness and acidity of the nutrient solution every day, trying to keep a fixed schedule. Record the results in a diary to keep a record of changes.

When there are nutrients in the tank, you cannot get an effective measurement using litmus paper or similar systems. For an accurate reading from the instruments, test the water after the nutrients have passed through the system at least once (preferably twice).

Change the pH of the solution using products to increase or decrease the acidity of the water.

NOTE: Any change in acidity affects the hardness of the water. The most effective acidity is between 5.5 and 6.2, never go above 6.5 and never go below 5.5, whatever vegetables you are growing.

Use a fixed residue meter in parts per million (TDS/PPM) or an EC meter (electrical conductivity) to test the hardness of the solution. If it is too hard, add water. If it is too soft, add fertilizer. Re-test with each change.

Replace/repack the solution in the tank when the fixed residue indicator in ppm shows values below the plants' needs.

Top-up fertilizers should not be used more than 3 or 4 times between total fertilizer changes. Do not use fertilizers indicated for replacement instead of top-up fertilizers.

It is good practice to have a hydroponic tank of the same volume or a volume greater than the empty volume of the plant/bath. For example, if you use a 20L system, you must use a minimum 20L tank. You can also use more, up to twice as much. The volume of the medium should not be calculated in the total volume. The larger the tank (with reasonableness), the better.

There is no specific lifespan of the fertilizer, as it depends on its volume and on how much the plant requires, as well as the transpiration rate of the plant. Each of these factors can vary substantially.

When you replace the fertilizer, you can use the water stored in the tank to water the plants grown in the soil.

Hydroponic plants do their best outdoors, but weather conditions may not allow it. When growing outdoors, rainwater or other types of water must be prevented from infiltrating and diluting the solution. If you cultivate indoors, you may need artificial light sources.

Tips

Make sure the fertilizers used in the hydroponic system are complete. Try to match the type of solution and water hardness to the water requirement.

Keep the temperature of the nutrient solution between 21/21 C°. These are ideal figures, but even if the water reaches 12 C° the plant will grow, only the growth will be slower.

Oxygenation of the nutrient solution is essential for proper fertilizer uptake. If possible, try to get the nutrients back into the reservoir, that will be enough. If this cannot be done, use an aquarium air pump.

The amount of nutrients that pass through the system every day depends on the type of plant, its size/maturity, the presence of fruit, humidity and air temperature.

It is a good idea to run some still water or with 1/4 of fertilizer once or twice between complete replacement to smooth out any fertilizer overdose. Remember that this can dilute the nutrient solution, so tests and modifications should be carried out after topping up.

Some water treatment plants have recently switched from chlorine to chloramine. They do this because it is cheaper and because it does not evaporate like Chlorine. If you ask a treatment company to say that it "evaporates in 2-3 days" but if you do some research on the internet you will find that "it does not evaporate, but it can break down into potentially dangerous by-products". You'll need a filter that can eliminate chloramine. Standard RO filters are not good, you will need to use one that contains a filter for Chloramine.

Tap water contains chemicals that can affect plant growth. If you smell chlorine or are unsure, it is best to keep the water in the air for 24 hours so that the substance evaporates. If you use a product to remove chlorine from aquariums, all you will do is add other chemicals to the water. Breathing the water will allow it to reach room temperature, reducing the possibility of thermal shock in contact with the plant root system.

Do not water less than two times a day (morning and afternoon), but you may need one every two hours. In order to have a safe guide look at the leaves, if they become saggy you need another watering.

A wide reservoir better maintains changes in fixed residue, electrical conductivity, water and acidity. Better to create a large tank.

Warnings

Some municipalities purify water with chlorine and bromine, substances that can damage plants. To get rid of bromine, simply fill a basin (not the reservoir) with cold water and let it rest overnight. If the next day you notice that bubbles have formed on the sides of the basin, tap it to release them into the air. This method is called perking, and it is very effective and cheap.

The chlorine in the tap water does not kill plants, on the contrary it can be useful to prevent mould and silt from settling on the bottom.

Before using tank / pipes / tanks / pumps, sterilize them by pouring boiling water on them. This will be especially useful if the tank has become infected. With the right care, the system will not become infected.

If you add new fertilizer to an existing nutrient solution, be careful, because you may add more micronutrients than you need. This process could cause problems for your plants. Some fertilizer manufacturers sell 'top-up' fertilizers made specifically for this purpose. If you can't get top-up fertilizer, use fertilizer that is leachable from plants grown in the soil.

Plants overdose quickly. An undernourished plant can last longer than an overdosed plant but can suffer from nutrient deficiencies.

Do not use products intended for the same purpose but from different manufacturers. Each producer has his or her own specifications and using two different ones could cause sensitive plant and plant imbalances.

Chlorine is released quickly when water is shaken in the open air.

CHAPTER 9 - Plant Nutrition

Hydroponics is undoubtedly one of the most innovative and efficient techniques for gardening and indoor garden cultivation.

But to maintain a perfect small indoor garden you need to use fertilising solutions to feed your decorative seedlings or fruit vegetables consistently and in the right way. In addition to mineral or chemical fertilizers, there are various products on the market, of organic and biological origin, suitable for every type of plant and vegetative phase.

Natural Fertilizers for Hydroponic Cultivation

With this system you can control the life cycle and development of your plants, keeping the variables of moisture, light and nutrients constant. The harmony between these factors is decisive in obtaining strong and vigorous plants, healthy and quality vegetables, lush and fragrant medicinal herbs.

Whatever crop you choose for hydroponic cultivation, there are various fertilizers that offer your plants the right nutrients.

As with plants grown on the ground, the right supply of mineral salts and nutrients is essential for plants grown above ground.

The main ones are:

- ✓ nitrogen.
- ✓ phosphorus.
- ✓ potassium.
- ✓ calcium.
- ✓ magnesium.

These elements (or rather macro-elements) must not be missing during all the vegetative and development phases of the plant. These nutrients, then, must be accompanied by other necessary nutrients (called micronutrients), which vary depending on the type of plant and the growth phase in which it is located:

- ✓ manganese;
- ✓ iron;
- ✓ sulphur;
- ✓ zinc;
- ✓ boron;
- ✓ molybdenum.

In hydroponic cultivation, all the nutrients, which the soil usually releases spontaneously, must be controlled and managed manually in a correct way. This operation may seem complex to newbies, but with the right guidance, the management of a hydroponic mini- greenhouse can become very simple and intuitive. On the market you can find the nutritive solutions to dissolve in water, in the right quantity and according to the doses indicated on the product label.

How to use Fertilizers for Hydroponic Growing

The technique of hydroponic cultivation is increasingly widespread, not only in agriculture, but also in private homes, where it is not always possible to have a small garden or vegetable garden on the balcony, precisely because of its many advantages: the versatility of the system; the excellent results in the production of inflorescence; the absence of pests and diseases related to the exposure of plants to the outside air; the economy and simplicity of management of the system. Without the constraint of seasonality, then, it is possible to have all year-round vegetables typical of the summer season (such as tomatoes, zucchini, aubergines, etc.), immediately ready for consumption and with a genuine taste.

With the hydroponic system (often erroneously associated with hydroponics), therefore, it is possible to take advantage of any environment or reduced space in the house and create a small green oasis, rich in scents, colours, fruits and vegetables to be consumed fresh and used in the kitchen with peace of mind. But to get the most out of your hydroponic mini- greenhouse you need to keep some fundamental factors under control:

- ✓ lighting.
- ✓ temperature.
- ✓ humidity level.
- ✓ air circulation.
- ✓ presence of the right amount of fertilizer.

pH and EC level (electrical conductivity, which determines the salinity of the nutrient solution, i.e. the amount of dissolved salts) of the substrate.

All these factors are crucial to keep your plants healthy and prevent the formation of mould or fungi. In particular, then, taking care to administer the right amount of nutrient solution, in the correct time and manner, is vital for the growth and well-being of all plants.

And just for a correct use of fertilizers, there are some useful tricks to observe.

First, remember that the fertilizing solution must be administered in different dosages according to the vegetative phase of the plant.

The nutrient solution to be given to the plants should always be diluted in water and introduced into the irrigation system, so that it is evenly distributed in the substrate. You can use running tap water, provided it is of good quality.

Also, remember to observe the doses indicated on the label or suggested by your nurseryman: an excessive amount of fertiliser, just like an insufficient amount, risks irreparably damaging your plants.

Finally, it is important to remember to check at regular intervals the pH and CE value of the substrate, which may be subject to fluctuations.

Advantages of Fertilizers

Fertilizers for the hydroponic system provide the macro and microelements useful to grow plants in an optimal way during each vegetative phase.

Among the different products commercially available for hydroponic cultivation, there are several compounds that stimulate seed germination and the rooting of cuttings in coconut fibre and other substrates.

There are different types of fertilisers that are generally diluted in water and fed into the irrigation system of hydroponic greenhouses. The best nutrient solution should be chosen according to the type of plant and its vegetative phase.

In decorative plants with inflorescence, fertilizers with low nitrogen and high potassium content increase production and flower quality.

CONCLUSION

Thank you for making it through to the end of this book, let's hope it was informative and able to provide you with all the tools you need to achieve your goals whatever they may be.

Hydroponics has emerged as a great way to lose growing genuine and tasty vegetable products at home for good health. Yet, many people fail to get all the benefits of this wonderful process due to lack of knowledge of the process. This book has tried to bring all the important points to the fore so that you can get all the benefits of hydroponics without having to deal with the negative effects.

All you must do is follow the information provided in the book and follow the directions.

You can also get all the benefits of the process by following the simple steps in the book.

I hope that this book will really help you achieve your goals.

Nicolas Campos

© Copyright 2020 by Nicolas Campos

Nicolas Campos

AQUAPONICS

FOR

BEGINNERS

How to Build Your Own Aquaponic System and Raise Fish and Plants Together. Produce Healthy to eat Healthy

INTRODUCTION

Aquaponics is the method of growing crops in water integrated with fish farming that provides all the necessary mineral nutrients. The good thing is that the entire cultivation process is highly automated, but still requires very strict management.

Aquaponics is preferable because it uses water and nutrients from aquaculture, especially since both are applied directly to the roots of the plant.

The availability of lighting is also an important component in agricultural production. Adequate lighting is achieved by planting crops in vertical structures so that accessibility to light is maximised, while density and shading are kept to a minimum.

These growing conditions for plant cultivation, in terms of water, nutrients and light, are ideal for crops and will maximise the usefulness of the growing area and use space that might otherwise be unused. Having a mobile multi-level cultivation structure exposes plants to ideal lighting always during the growing season.

CHAPTER 1 - Aquaponics

Due to climate change and the international economic crisis, there is a clear need for the agri-food sector to identify new strategies to ensure more sustainable production in line with new market needs. Farmers and agricultural producers are in fact called upon to face the challenges arising from climate change and its effects on the environment, biodiversity and the living conditions of the population. The water scarcity that has affected various regions of the world in recent years has put farmers and fish farmers under severe strain, with their production reduced or greatly damaged. In this context, aquaponics could represent a real possibility for the development of this sector. But what is aquaponics and how does it work?

What is Aquaponics?

If we want to cut short we could give an answer like this: "Aquaponics is the marriage between aquaculture (fish farming) and hydroponic plant growth in water, in the absence of soil)" Put together in an integrated system and, since we have integrated the system, why not also integrate the name? Aquaponics then.

Therefore, aquaponics can be defined as the union between aquaculture and hydroponics. The latter is a practice in which plants are grown without soil, using only water enriched with all the nutrients that plants need. In the case of aquaponics, the basic nutrients for plant growth are provided by fish farming, of which these substances are the main waste products. In this system, elements such as nitrogen and phosphorus, resulting both from excretion and excretion of fish and from decomposition of uningested feed, can be absorbed by the roots of growing plants directly immersed in the water.

Aquaponics is not a new cultivation technique; in fact, it is since the 70s that we have started to talk about this technique in a substantial way. However, it is only in recent years that it has returned to the forefront, thanks also to new scientific research and greater attention to sustainability on the part of consumers and producers.

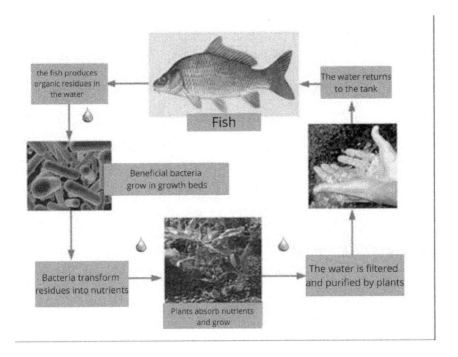

the fish produces organic residues in the water

Fish

The water returns to the tank

Beneficial bacteria grow in growth beds

Bacteria transform residues into nutrients

Plants absorb nutrients and grow

The water is filtered and purified by plants

How does Aquaponics work?

An aquaponic system is a recirculation system, where the water, thanks to the use of one or more pumps, is taken from the tank in which the fish are bred and passed through a biofilter. The latter allows to start the nitrification process that will lead to the formation of nitrites and nitrates then assimilated by the plants. In addition, it will reduce as much as possible the quantity of suspended solids, which is very important in order to maintain the good quality of the water and avoid the lowering of the dissolved oxygen in it. The water is then introduced into the cultivation beds in which the cultivated plants are present (whose roots are in direct contact with the water) and finally reintroduced into the breeding tank.

There are many varieties of cultivated plants, not only leafy vegetables but also plants such as zucchini, aubergines, tomatoes or aromatic herbs. Likewise, it is possible to breed almost all freshwater fish species in aquaponics, from trout to carp (but also ornamental species such as Koi carp) or even species that are exotic to us such as tilapia. It is also possible to breed various species of crustaceans such as the Austropotamobius pallipes crayfish in aquaponics. Depending on the animal and plant species chosen, the system should be calibrated to ensure the correct supply of nutrients to the plants.

Aquaponics can be understood as a sustainable agricultural production activity in which the cycles of the main macronutrients are closed through the integration of two production systems, aquaculture and hydroponics. Compared to conventional farming techniques, aquaponics has several strengths, including:

Water saving aquaponics uses about 90% less water than traditional agriculture.

Small spaces: As plants do not need soil, aquaponics allows intensive cultivation in relatively small spaces.

No use of pesticides and pesticides: aquaponics does not include their use. In order to avoid problems of toxicity to fish and plants, biological control is used in aquaponics to control parasites. In addition, an attempt is made to isolate the production system as well as possible from the surrounding environment in order to limit the entry of pests and pathogens.

No fertiliser use: plant nutrients are provided by fish farming

Emissions control: there is no need to use agricultural vehicles, resulting in lower consumption of fossil fuels.

What are the limits of aquaponics?

The main limits of aquaponics concern two fundamental aspects: the complexity of the production system and its economic sustainability. Being an integrated production system, aquaponics requires expertise from the farmer/breeder both in the cultivation of plant species and in fish farming.

From an economic point of view, aquaponics can generate a double profit for those who practice it by placing two different types of products (vegetables and fish) on the market. On the other hand, the need to allocate these systems inside greenhouses or protected structures and to condition the temperature in order to guarantee a constant production during the year, increase production costs. But now this is the price that consumers must get used to paying for a truly sustainable product.

Which plants can be grown with aquaponics?

There are many varieties of plants that can be grown with the aquaponics method, potentially all of them; in particular all those - as seen above - that do not need any special support to grow, including broad-leaved vegetables, salads, zucchini, aubergines and aromatic herbs.

Which fish for aquaponics?

For fish that can be used within an aquaculture system, you can choose any type of freshwater fish, including shrimps. Of course, depending on the type of fish chosen, it is necessary to set the system differently, according to the characteristics of the variety chosen, in order to ensure the right amount and type of nutrients to the plants.

What does it take to create an aquaculture plant?

To build an aquaculture plant from scratch you need to buy a tank for fish farming, a hydroponic tank with a pump - which will be placed above the fish tank - in which you will place the plants, bacteria that allow you to decompose the waste fish, filters, a kit to measure and adjust the pH, supplements to solve any problems and nutritional deficiencies and then of course the fish you prefer and the plants to be grown.

To start and start with peace of mind an aquaculture, it is advisable to buy a system and ready-to-use kits, which will only need to be assembled and set up following the instructions in the package. Generally speaking, starting and maintenance of an aquaponic system does not require great care and attention, but - like all crops of this type, including hydroponics and aeroponics - it requires some controls, such as proper temperature, pH, humidity, proper ventilation and aeration, cleaning of surfaces and the right amount of nutrients.

One of the important aspects to consider at the beginning, in fact, is precisely the relationship - which must be well balanced - between the number and type of plants chosen and the number and breed of fish you wish to breed. In this way you can ensure a healthy and efficient environment. The other factor to keep in mind always is the nutrition provided to the fish, which must be of high quality and supplied in the right doses in order to guarantee the balance of the environment.

Main applications of Aquaponics

The technique of soil cultivation in aquaponic ecosystem allows to grow 100% organic plants with different application methods depending on the desired crops.

Vertical Aquaponics Vertical Growing

Vertical cultivation increases the convenience of the plant cost on the available space, optimizing the human labour cost. Vertical cultivation can be used to seasonally or deseasonally adjust plant production (light conditions and controlled environment).

How much does vertical aquaponic cultivation produce?

- Lettuce: 95 kg/m2 each year
- Chard: 75 kg/m2 each year
- Strawberries: 4.9Kg/m2 each month (Seascape)
- Basil: 1.88 kg/m2 per week Vs 0.15 kg/m2 of ground cultivation!

ZipGrow is a patented vertical hydroponic technology designed for high density agricultural production. The growth towers ensure the maximization of crop production, which is up to 4 times more intense than traditional techniques. The vertical towers consist of a rigid casing that contains the multifunctional Matrix Media. It is a growing substrate as well as a mechanical and biological filter.

The matrix inside each tower is an essential component of the system, their surface area is much larger than any other inert, this allows a greater nitrifying and filtering power, which is the basis of high-density production. The length of these matrices is 1,50 mt making it very easy to install and maintain, moreover it is composed by 93% air, allowing the water to move freely inside.

The thrust of the water dissolves oxygen inside it, thus eliminating the formation of anaerobic zones, which are harmful for an aquaponic cultivation plant because they tend to cause plant roots to die, cause foul-smelling compounds such as hydrogen sulphite and are home to some pathogenic organisms. Open spaces and good percolation, on the contrary, allow a more stable temperature in the roots, which is the basis of plant health.

Why choose vertical cultivation?

Current agricultural practices are unsustainable:

- Water is treated as an infinite resource.
- Our agricultural efforts absorb resources such as water and land and make obvious use of pesticides.
- Between 38 and 50% of harvested produce is lost to deterioration.

Nutrient Film Technique

The Nutrient Film Technique is a cultivation technique that uses horizontal PVC pipes, in each of which passes a film of water rich in nutrients. One of the advantages of using this technique is its low evaporation, as the water is completely shielded from the sun.

Holes are drilled in the pipe, in which the plants will be placed. As soon as they receive the nutrient flow, they start to develop the root system inside the pipe, at the same time the stems and leaves start to grow all around.

The NFT does not use inerts, so the water passing through the pipes must necessarily be treated beforehand, so a mechanical separator and a biofilter are required.

The maximum flow rate, within each pipe, must always be controlled and should never exceed 1-2 litres/minute.

In this project will be used no. 6 φ110 ducts, each of which will have a length of 5.00 m and a slope of about 1 cm/m. The holes inside each pipe have a diameter of about 8 cm and a wheelbase of 50 cm. The distance between two pipes will be 1.0 m to allow the passage of one person.

The NFT channels/pipes will be raised from the ground with adjustable structures, in order to create a natural waterfall for the collection of wastewaters and the natural recirculation to the collection tank, equipped with a submersible pump.

Growth Bed

Growth beds are a technique used for high-medium-stem crops or for plants that produce large and/or heavy fruits. The aggregates used inside these beds in fact act both as support for the roots of the plants and as filtration, in theory, mechanics and biology.

The mechanical filtration of these aggregates may be lacking in cases where the density of fish is very high. For this reason and for safety reasons, it was preferred to use a mechanical separator located inside the fish tanks.

The weak points of this technique are essentially two: the high evaporation of the water and the weight of the aggregates. However, if you want to cultivate certain types of plants there is no alternative: even in the trunk tree area the technique used is precisely that of the growth beds (in structure more similar to pots than "beds" proper), as the mechanical resistance of the Aquaponic is the only one among the cultivation techniques capable of bearing the weight of a trunk tree.

The structure of the growth beds (in the dedicated thematic area) will be made of laminated wood, covered with food-grade polyethylene, to guarantee the hydraulic seal. There is a total of 4 growth beds, all measuring 0.70 mt x 4.50 mt x 0.30 mt; the inert material chosen is expanded clay, given its chemical-physical characteristics. The density of cultivation that can be reached with this method strongly depends on the type of plant used: it varies from a value of 6 plants/m2 in the case of watermelons, up to values of about 200 plants/m2 in the case of saffron.

Fundamental in order to guarantee the movement of water within the system is the siphon.

The siphon allows the water to rise to a specific level, allowing the roots of the plants to take all the nutrients present in it and, once the maximum height has been reached, triggering it allows the tank to be emptied by sending the water to the return tank.

Deep water culture

Functioning:

The nutrient-rich water is circulated through long channels at a depth of about 20 cm while the rafts (usually polystyrene) float on top. The plants are supported inside holes in the rafts. The roots of the plants hang in nutrient-rich, oxygenated water, where they absorb large amounts of oxygen and nutrients that contribute to fast growing conditions.

This method is the most common in large scale distribution, when you tend to grow a specific crop (typically lettuce, salad leaves or basil) and where you have a high density of fish (up to 10-20 kg of fish per m3 of aquarium). However, it can be adapted to a low-density coefficient of fish production.

The water flows by gravity from the fish tanks, through the mechanical filter and into the biofilter. The water is pumped in two directions through a "Y" connector. Some water is pumped directly into the fish tank, the remaining water is distributed equally through the channels. The water flows, again by gravity, through the growth channels where the plants are located and then out of the channels and back into the biofilter, where it is pumped back into the tank or fish channels.

However, when using a low fish density, the DWC can be designed without the use of external, mechanical or biological filtration containers. In this system, water flows by gravity from the fish tanks directly into the DWC channels.

Advantages:

The main advantage of the DWC is the amortisation of all initial costs.

It is a good alternative for beginner growers interested in growing above ground. In addition, let us not forget that the most important results will be achieved at harvest time. Higher nutrient uptake also means plants with higher quality buds, higher yields and a more intense "high". Soil cultivation will never be able to compete with hydroponic cultivation, as the roots do not receive the same amount of oxygen provided by a constant flow of air. Moreover, it is a system that can be expanded. The principle is also the same for growing several plants.

CHAPTER 2 - Advantages and Disadvantages

Advantages of Aquaponic Growing

The advantages of aquaponics are many, let's analyse them together:

Few resources

One of the most considered is its ability to grow different types of food using very few resources in the process. In fact, it is a natural and organic process.

Minimum use of electricity

To operate an aquaponic cultivation system you need power, but there are few pieces of equipment that require energy. This leads to low net energy consumption.

Minimum water use

Even less water is used because most aquaponics systems are recirculated, which means that the water is circulated through the system instead of being disposed of after use.

The loss of primary water in aquaponic systems is minimal because it comes from evaporation and transpiration of the plants.

No use of pesticides and chemicals

Equally important is that in many systems the need for pesticides and other chemicals is low and sometimes not needed at all.

Aquaponics systems are designed for use in a controlled environment, such as a greenhouse or indoor warehouse, and the process by which bacteria convert fish waste into plant food or nutrients eliminates the need for fertilizers. The pH is also adjusted by itself within the system through the process of conversion by the bacteria.

Disadvantages of Aquaponic Growing

Of course, it's not all pink and flowers, there are also disadvantages in aquaponic cultivation. Let's go together and see what they are.

Non-economic start-up cost

The start-up cost is often higher than what people want to spend on the cultivation system.

While you may think that these systems are cheap, you will notice that systems at the practitioner's level tend to be quite expensive. However, this expense begins to pay for itself as you start enjoying fresh produce after a short time.

Difficulties in choosing the system best suited to our needs

The choices between the available systems can be quite difficult to make. While you may think that there is only one system style, you will quickly find more systems available.

A simple choice in the wrong system, however, can lead to a disaster because the system will not be suitable for the use you want to make of it.

Daily Maintenance

Daily checks must be carried out on systems, lights and pipes. These checks will help to ensure that the system is working properly but will also help to ensure that everything is working properly. Without this type of control, people may have trouble understanding why their plants are not thriving.

Is it good to grow in aquaponics?

Aquaponic systems are an easy way to grow food.

Daily maintenance is necessary, but once the system is in operation, the main activity, day by day, is to feed the fish and check for signs of change in the balance of the system. Monitoring water chemistry, temperature and nutrient levels and moving to correct them as needed will maintain a thriving aquaponic system.

I recommend starting with the type of cultivation that meets your needs and expectations.

Nicolas Campos

CHAPTER 3 - Types of Aquaponic System

This chapter illustrates drawings related to the design of different aquaponics systems. There are many design aspects to consider, to consider all environmental and biological factors that have an impact on the aquaponic ecosystem. The purpose of this chapter is to present all these aspects in the most accessible way in order to provide a comprehensive explanation of each component of an aquaponic system.

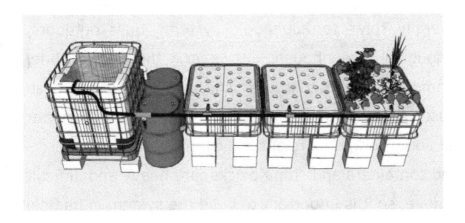

Floating Root Planting Drawing (DWC)

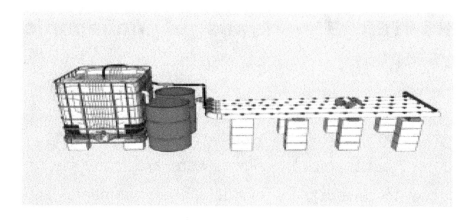

Drawing a small plant (NFT)

Choice of location

The choice of site is an important aspect in the installation of an aquaponic system. In this section we generally refer to aquaponic systems built outdoors, without a greenhouse. However, there are brief comments on greenhouses and shading using mesh structures for larger units. It is important to remember that some components of the system, particularly water-filled containers and stone blocks, are heavy and difficult to move, so it is important to build the system in its final position. The locations identified must be on a stable, horizontal surface, in an area that is protected from bad weather but well exposed to sunlight.

Make sure you choose a site that is stable and level. Some of the main components of an aquaponic system are heavy, there is a real risk that the legs of the system will sink into the ground. This can lead to the interruption of water flow, flooding or a catastrophic collapse of the system. It is therefore essential to find a flat, solid ground. Implanting everything on a concrete surface can be a solution, but it has the disadvantage of not being able to pass any of the components underground, therefore with the risk of tripping. If the system is placed on the ground, it is useful to cover everything with sheets that prevent the growth of weeds. In addition, it may be essential to place concrete or cement blocks under the legs of the grow beds to improve their stability.

Exposition

Extreme environmental conditions can stress plants and destroy structures. Strong winds can have a considerable negative impact on plant production and can cause damage to stem and reproductive parts.

In addition, heavy rain can damage plants and unprotected electrical outlets. Large amounts of rain can dilute nutrient-rich water and can flood the system if there is no overflow mechanism. Snow causes the same problems as heavy rainfall, with the added threat of cold damage. It is advisable that the system is in a protected wind zone. If heavy rainfall is usual, it may be worth protecting the system with a plastic cover (tunnel or greenhouse).

Sunlight is crucial for plants, which need to receive the optimal amount of sunlight during the day. Most common aquaponic systems grow well in full sunlight; however, if the sunlight is too intense, a simple structure that allows shading can be installed above the growing beds. Some photosensitive plants, including lettuce, and some cabbages may rise to seed due to too much sun or become bitter or take a bad taste. Other tropical plants, such as turmeric and some ornamental plants may show burns on the leaves when exposed to too much sun and therefore produce better if they can be placed in half shade. On the opposite side, with little sunlight, some plants can have slow growth rates. Therefore, we should be careful to build the aquaponic plants in a sunny position. If a shaded area is the only one available, it is recommended that suitable species are planted.

The systems should be designed to take advantage of the moving sun in the sky from east to west. Generally, growth beds should be spatially arranged so that the longest side is on the north-south axis. This is more efficient than the sun during the day. Alternatively, if it is preferable to have less light, depending on the type of crop, orient the beds, tubes and channels following the east-west axis. Also pay attention to the layout of the plants, which should not inadvertently become one with the other.

Unlike plants, fish do not need direct sunlight. On the contrary, it is important that the fish tanks are in the shade, which is why they are usually covered with shading sheets.

Shading helps to keep the water temperature stable and prevent algae from growing, covering fish tanks also prevents debris or leaves from falling into them and prevents intrusion by ichthyophagous animals.

Location

When choosing the site, it is important to consider the availability of connections to the services. Electrical sockets are required for water and air pumps that must be protected from water and equipped with a "lifesaving" device to reduce the risk of electric shock.

In addition, the water supply to the system should be easily accessible, whether it is for connections to the municipal network or rainwater collection tanks.

Although extremely efficient in terms of water resources, aquaponic systems require water additions from time to time, filters should also be rinsed. If an aquaponic system were located near a 'traditional' crop, it would benefit from rinsing the filters, which are always rich in nutrients. The system should also be placed where it is easy to access every day because frequent monitoring and daily feeding of the fish is necessary. Finally, consider fencing the entire system to prevent theft and vandalism, the entry of predatory animals and for compliance with any food safety rules.

Shading Structures

Having a greenhouse is not essential for a small aquaponic system but having a roof can be useful because it lengthens the production season. This is particularly true in colder temperate regions, greenhouses can also be used to maintain a warm water temperature during the cold months, allowing year-round production.

A greenhouse is a metal, wood or plastic frame that is covered with transparent nylon, plastic or glass. The purpose of this structure is to allow sunlight (solar radiation) to enter the greenhouse and remain "trapped" in it, thus heating the air inside the greenhouse. When the sun goes down, the heat is retained in the greenhouse by the roof and walls, allowing a warmer and more stable temperature throughout the 24 hours. Greenhouses also provide environmental protection against wind, snow and driving rain. In greenhouses, the growing season can be extended by maintaining solar heat, but they can also be heated from the inside. Greenhouses can also keep animals and other pests away. Greenhouses are comfortable for working during the cold season and offer the farmer protection from the weather. All in all, these advantages can be summed up in increased productivity and a longer farming season.

However, these advantages must be offset by the negative aspects of greenhouses. The initial investment costs for a greenhouse can be high depending on the desired degree of technology and sophistication. Greenhouses also require additional operating costs because fans are needed to create air circulation to prevent overheating and excessive humidity conditions.

Fish tanks

Fish tanks are a key component in any plant and can account for up to 20 percent of the total cost. Fish require certain conditions to live and thrive and therefore fish tanks must be chosen carefully. There are several important aspects to consider such as shape, material and colour.

The shape of the tank

Although any shape would be fine, round tubs with flat bottoms are the best. The round shape allows the water to circulate evenly and at the same time the solid waste is conveyed to the centre of the tank by centripetal force. Flat-bottomed square tanks are also acceptable, but they require more work in solid waste removal. Other tanks, artistic and non-geometric in shape, with many curves can create dead spots where there is water without circulation. These areas can collect waste and create dangerous anoxic conditions for fish. If you must use irregularly shaped tanks it may be necessary to add water or air pumps to ensure proper circulation and remove solids. It is also important to choose a tank that adapts to the characteristics of the aquatic species kept some species have better growth and less stress with adequate space available.

Material

The use of inert plastic or fibreglass is recommended for their long life. Avoid metal due to rust. Plastic and fibreglass tanks are interesting to install (also for hydraulic connections) and are quite light and easy to handle. They are commonly used, even old containers (plastic tanks for transporting liquids and blue bins) as they tend to be cheap. If you use such containers make sure they are UV resistant because direct sunlight can destroy plastic. Generally, low density polyethylene (LDPE) tanks are preferable because of their high resistance and the characteristics that allow them to be used for food. LDPE in fact, is the most used material for water tanks for civil use. Another option is an earth pond. Natural ponds are very difficult to manage for aquaponic plants because the natural biological process that occurs inside the substrate and in the mud at the bottom can be difficult to govern and its nutrients are often already used by aquatic plants. Cement or plastic lined ponds are much more acceptable and can be an economical option.

Soil ponds can make hydraulic operations difficult and plumbing design should be carefully considered before embracing this option. One of the simplest ponds is a hole dug into the ground, lined with bricks or concrete blocks, and then lined

with a waterproof coating like polyethylene plastic. Other options include second-hand containers such as bathtubs, drums or bulk containers. It is very important to ensure that the container has not previously been used for toxic materials to prevent any trace of it remaining. So, choose a used container carefully, best if you know the seller.

The colour white or other light colours are strongly recommended as they allow easy control of the fish to check its behaviour and the amount of waste deposited on the bottom of the tank. White tanks also reflect sunlight and keep the water cooler. Alternatively, the outside of dark coloured tanks can be painted white. In very hot or cold areas, it may be necessary to further insulate the tanks thermally.

Fish tanks should be covered. The shade prevents algae from growing. In addition, the cover serves to prevent the fish from jumping out (this often occurs with freshly inserted fish or if the water quality is not optimal), the cover also serves to prevent leaves and debris from falling into the tanks and to prevent predators such as cats and birds from attacking the fish. Shading nets are often used for agriculture that block up to 80-90 percent of the sunlight. Shading nets can be secured to a simple wooden frame to provide weight, prevent the wind from moving them and at the same time allow easy removal.

Safety and redundancy

The first precaution to be taken with respect to fish tanks is to prevent them from losing water, with the danger of losing all the fish. Even if some accidents are inevitable (for example a tree falling on the tank), mistakes with more serious effects are almost always due to the "human factor". Therefore, make sure that there is no possibility for the operator to discharge the water inadvertently. If the water pump is in the fish tank, never place it on the bottom so that the tank cannot be brought to dry. Always use a hose inside the tank to ensure a minimum water level.

Filtering

Mechanical filtering

For a recirculation system, mechanical filtration is undoubtedly the most important aspect of the project. From a mechanical point of view, filtration is the separation and removal of suspended solids and fish waste from tanks. Removing this waste is essential for the health of the system, because otherwise, if solid waste is broken down into fish tanks, harmful gases released by anaerobic bacteria would be released. In addition, the waste can clog the systems and disrupt the water flow, causing anoxic conditions that are hostile to root development.

Small-scale aquaponic systems generally have a lower stocking density than the traditional recirculation fish farming systems for which these mechanical filters were originally designed, but a certain level of mechanical filtration is also essential for aquaponic fish tanks, regardless of the type of hydroponic method used.

There are different types of mechanical filters. The simplest method is a screen or filter between the fish tank and the growth beds. This filter catches solid waste and must be rinsed frequently.

Similarly, the water leaving the fish tank can pass through a small container of particulate matter, separated from the growth bed; this container is easier to rinse periodically.

Both these methods are valid for some small-scale aquaponic systems, but are insufficient in larger systems with more fish, where the amount of solid waste is significant.

There are many types of mechanical filters, sedimentation tanks, radial flow filters, sand or bead filters, etc. each can be used depending on the amount of solid waste that needs to be removed. However, since this publication focuses on small-scale aquaponic systems, sedimentation tanks and mechanical separators are the most appropriate filters.

Sedimentation tanks, in general, can remove up to 60 percent of total solids. For more information on the different mechanical filtration methods, see the additional reading section at the end of this publication.

Mechanical Separators

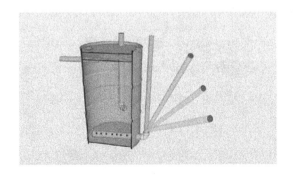

A mechanical separator is a dedicated vessel that uses the properties of water to separate particles. Generally, water that moves slower is not capable of carrying as many particles as fast flowing water. Therefore, the separator is constructed to accelerate and slow down the water so that the particles concentrate at the bottom and can be removed. In a separator turbulence is created, water from the fish tank enters close to the centre of gravity through a pipe. This pipe is positioned tangentially to the container and forces the water to swirl in a circular motion inside the container. The centripetal force created by the circular movement of the water forces the solid waste into the water at the centre and bottom of the container, because the water in the centre of the vortex is slower than the water outside. Once this happens the waste is collected at the bottom. A hose attached to the bottom of the container can be opened periodically, allowing solid waste to be removed from the container and used for traditional watering. The cleaned water comes out of the top separator and enters the biofilter or growth beds.

The trapped and removed solid waste contains nutrients and is very useful for traditional crops or garden plants in general. As a general guideline, for small-scale plants the size of the mechanical separator should be about one sixth of the volume of the fish tank but many factors such as the storage density of the fish and the design of the tank and the separator itself influence the size. Appendix 8 will contain detailed, step-by-step instructions for the construction of each part of these systems.

Proper preliminary mechanical filtration is particularly important for NFT and DWC units and serves to intercept and remove solid waste. Without this preliminary process, the solid waste in suspension would accumulate in vegetable growth pipes and canals and suffocate the roots. The accumulation of solid waste causes blockages in the pumps and hydraulic components. Finally, as mentioned, unfiltered waste can create anaerobic points in the circuit that threaten the system. These anaerobic zones can in fact lead to the development of bacteria that produce hydrogen sulphide, a toxic and lethal gas for fish, due to the fermentation of solid waste. The presence of dangerous anaerobic zones is often revealed by the smell of rotten eggs.

Biofiltration

Biofiltration is the conversion of ammonia and nitrite into nitrates by living bacteria. Most fish waste is not filterable using a mechanical filter because the waste is dissolved directly in the water and the size of these particles is too small to be removed mechanically. Therefore, an aquaponic system uses microscopic bacteria to treat this microscopic waste. Biofiltration is essential because in aquaponics ammonia and nitrite are toxic even at low concentrations, while plants need nitrates to grow. In an aquaponic system, the biofilter is deliberately designed to accommodate as many living bacteria as possible. In addition, the movement of water within a biofilter will be useful to break down very fine solids not extracted from the separator.

Separate biofiltration is not necessary in a medium bed cultivation technique (e.g. expanded clay) because the grow beds themselves are perfect biofilters.

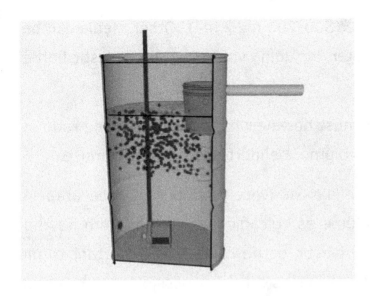

The biofilter is designed to have a large surface area fed with well oxygenated water. The biofilter is installed between the mechanical filter and the containers in which the hydroponic culture takes place. The minimum volume of the biofilter should be one sixth of that of the fish tank.

The "mediom" commonly used in the biofilter is Bioballs® a registered product available in aquaculture shops, there are also generic brands.

These products are designed to be an ideal biofilter material because they consist of small shaped plastic elements that have a very large surface area compared to their volume (500-700 m2 / m³). Other media can be used as a biofilter, including volcanic gravel, plastic bottle caps, etc.

Each biofilter must however have a high surface ratio in relation to its volume, be inert and be easy to rinse.

Bioballs® have almost twice as much surface area in relation to volume as volcanic lapillus, and both have a higher ratio to plastic bottle caps. It is important to fill the biofilter container as much as possible, but even so the surface area provided by the media may not be sufficient to ensure adequate biofiltration, so it is a good idea to oversize the biofilter during initial construction, but knowing that secondary biofilters can be added later if necessary. Biofilters need to be shaken from time to time to avoid clogging, as well as rinsed to avoid being clogged by solid waste that can create an anoxic zone.

Another 'ingredient' required for biofilter is aeration. Nitrifying bacteria need adequate access to oxygen to oxidise ammonia. A simple solution is to use an air pump, placing porous stones connected to an air inlet at the bottom of the container. This ensures that the bacteria have a constantly high concentration of dissolved oxygen. Air pumps can also help to break down any solid or suspended waste not captured by the mechanical separator by shaking and continuously moving the floating Bioballs®. To trap additional solids inside the biofilter, it is also possible to insert a small cylindrical plastic bucket with a nylon mesh, or sponges at the biofilter inlet.

The waste is trapped by this secondary mechanical filter, allowing water to flow over through small holes drilled in the bottom of the bucket into the biofilter container.

Mineralization

Mineralization, from the point of view of aquaponics, refers to the way solid waste is treated and metabolized by bacteria into plant nutrients. Solid waste that is trapped by the mechanical filter contains nutrients; although the processing of this waste is different from biofiltration which requires separate treatment. Keeping solids within the overall system increases the nutrients available to plants. Waste that remains in mechanical filters, biofilters or growth beds undergoes certain mineralization processes. Leaving the waste in place for longer allows for more mineralization. However, this same solid waste component, if not properly managed and mineralized, will block the water flow, consuming oxygen and leading to anoxic conditions, which in turn will produce dangerous hydrogen sulphide gas. Some large systems therefore deliberately leave the solid waste inside the filters, ensuring an adequate flow of water and oxygenation, so that maximum nutrients are released. However, this method is impractical for craft NFT and DWC systems.

If you decide to deliberately "mineralize" these solids, there are simple ways to assist the bacteria in the action in a separate container, simply by adequate oxygenation through air diffused by porous stones. After some time, the solid waste will be consumed, metabolized and transformed by heterotrophic bacteria. At this point, the water can flow back into the aquaponic system and the residual waste, which will be reduced in volume, can be added to the soil.

Alternatively, these solid wastes can be immediately separated, removed and added to any agricultural soil, garden or compost as a valuable fertilizer. However, immediately extracting these nutrients from the system can be the cause of deficiencies in plants that may require nutrient supplementation.

A compromise solution may be to use a grow bed (e.g. expanded clay or lapillus) for a combination of mechanical and biological filtration.

It is also possible to use a combination of a grow bed for mechanical and biofiltration followed by an NFT system and/or DWC unit.

This can be important where there is no possibility to have the necessary materials to make a turbulence separator and/or a separate biofilter. suffice it to say that for every 200 g of fish feed per day the biofilter must have a volume of 300 litres. The small gravel filter can provide adequate biofiltration for about 20 kg of fish. Although this grow bed would be adequate to provide adequate biofiltration for an NFT or DWC unit as well as capture and retain solid waste, an additional solid waste capture device inserted in the bed is sometimes recommended to prevent the grow bed from clogging itself with solids produced by fish in the long run.

Ultimately, since the beds should also be rinsed periodically to remove the solid waste, it is in any case better to provide easy to maintain mechanical filtration upstream of the grow beds.

Summing up

A certain level of filtration is essential for all aquaponic systems the amount of fish stored; the type of system determines the amount of filtration needed. Mechanical filters separate solid waste to avoid toxic accumulations and convert dissolved nitrogenous waste into nitrate through biofiltration.

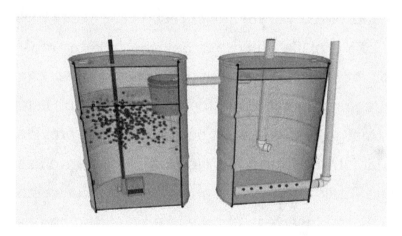

The grow beds themselves act both as mechanical filters and biofilters when using this technique, but additional mechanical filtration is sometimes necessary for high fish densities (15 kg / m3).

Without the grow beds, such as in NFT and DWC units, filtration is always necessary.

Mineralization of solid waste returns more nutrients to the system. Mineralization occurs naturally in grow beds, but in NFT and DWC systems it must be prepared in separate containers.

Nicolas Campos

CHAPTER 4 - Media Beds, NFT, DWC

Hydroponic component is the term to describe the section of the plant where the planets grow. There are several drawings, three of which are discussed in detail in this article. These three models are: medium bed unit, where plants grow in a substrate; nutrient film technique (NFT), where plants grow with their roots in large tubes with a water culture thread; and deep water culture (DWC), also called water raft or floating systems, where plants are suspended above a water reservoir using a floating raft. Each method has advantages and disadvantages. See Sections 4.3-4.6 for details of each.

Water movement is essential to keep all organisms alive in the aquaponics. The flow of water flows from the fish tanks, through the mechanical separator and biofilter and finally reaches the plants in their media beds, pipes or channels, which collect the dissolved nutrients.

If the water movement stops, the most immediate effect will be an OD reduction and the accumulation of waste in the fish tank.

A common guideline for densely populated aquaponic systems is to have two water changes per hour. For example, if an aquaponic unit has a total water volume of 1000 litres, the water flow rate should be 2000 litres/hr, so that every hour the water is renewed twice. However, in case of low storage density the water only needs to be recycled once every hour. There are three commonly used methods to keep water moving through a system: submersible impeller pumps, airlifts and human energy.

Water movement

The movement of water is essential to keep all organisms alive in the aquaponics. The flow of water flows from the fish tanks, through the mechanical separator and biofilter and finally reaches the plants in their media beds, pipes or channels, which collect the dissolved nutrients.

If the water movement stops, the most immediate effect will be an OD reduction and the accumulation of waste in the fish tank.

A common guideline for densely populated aquaponic systems is to have two water changes per hour. For example, if an aquaponic unit has a total water volume of 1000 litres, the water flow rate should be 2000 litres/hr, so that every hour the water is renewed twice. However, in case of low storage density the water only needs to be recycled once every hour. There are three commonly used methods to keep water moving through a system: submersible impeller pumps, airlifts and human energy.

Submersible water pump

The heart of an aquaponic system is almost always a submersible impeller pump, this type of pump is recommended.

In order to ensure a long service life and energy efficiency, high quality water pumps should preferably be used. High quality pumps can maintain their pumping capacity and efficiency for a period of 3-5 years, while lower quality products will lose pumping power in a shorter time and significantly reduce water flows. As far as flow rate is concerned, the small units described in this work need a flow rate of 2000 litre/h for a maximum height of 1.5 metres; a submersible pump of this capacity would have consumed 25-50 W/h.

A useful approximation to calculate the energy required for submersible pumps is that a pump can move 40 litres of water per hour for every watt per hour consumed, although some models are twice as efficient.

When designing the hydraulic sizing of the pump, it is important to realize that during pumping there is a loss of energy at each connection; up to 5 percent of the total flow rate can be lost at each pipe connection when water is forced through it. Therefore, use the minimum number of connections possible. It is also important to note that the smaller the pipe diameter, the greater the loss of water flow. A 30mm pipe has twice the flow rate of a 20mm pipe, even if served by pumps of the same capacity.

In addition, a larger pipe requires no maintenance to remove the accumulation of solids inside it. In practical terms, this translates into significant savings in electricity and operating costs. When installing an aquaponic system, be sure to place the submersible pump in an accessible location for periodic cleaning. In fact, the internal filter will need cleaning every 2-3 weeks. Submersible water pumps will break if they are operated without water.

Airlifts

Airlifts are another water lifting technique that uses an air pump rather than a water pump.

The air is forced to the bottom of a pipe inside the fish tank, the rising of the bubbles towards the surface allows the water to be carried along with them. One of the advantages is that airlifts are more energy efficient, but they can only lift water up to limited heights (30-40 cm). One advantage of airlifts is that they oxygenate the water during its transport through air bubbles.

Finally, air pumps generally have a longer life than submerged water pumps. Finally, there is the advantage that only one airlift pump can be purchased for both aeration and water circulation, which reduces the expense for a second pump.

Muscular strength

Some aquaponic systems are designed to use human force to move water.

Water can be lifted in buckets or using pulleys, modified bicycles or other means. An expansion vessel can be filled manually and placed to drain slowly throughout the day. These methods are only applicable for small systems and should only be considered if electricity is not available or is not reliable. Often these systems will have low OD and insufficient mixing of nutrients.

Ventilation

Air pumps inject air into the water through pipes and porous stones inside fish tanks, thus increasing OD levels in the water.

Additional dissolved oxygen is an essential component of NFT and DWC units. The air is diffused through small porous stones.

The smaller the bubbles, the better the oxygen will be distributed. Small bubbles have more surface area and therefore release water oxygen better than large bubbles; this makes the aeration system more efficient and contributes to cost containment. It is therefore recommended to use quality air stones in order to obtain small air bubbles. Air stones should be cleaned regularly first with a chlorine solution to kill bacterial deposits and then, if necessary, with a slightly acidic substance to remove mineralization or they should be replaced when the bubble flow is insufficient. The quality of air pumps is an irreplaceable component of aquaponic systems, many systems have been saved from catastrophic collapse by an abundance of OD.

For small units, consisting of a 1000 litre tank, it is recommended that at least two air lines with stones, also called injectors, are placed in the fish tank as well as an injector in the biofilter container.

Venturi Siphons

Low-tech and easy to build Venturi siphons are another technique to increase OD levels in aquaponic systems. This technique is particularly useful in DWC channels.

To put it simply, Venturi siphons use a hydrodynamic principle to "suck" air from outside (suction) when pressurized water flows at a higher speed through a smaller diameter pipe section. With constant water flow, if the diameter of the hose decreases, the water velocity must increase, and this higher velocity creates a negative pressure. Venturi siphons are short sections of pipe (20 mm diameter, 5 cm long) inserted into the main pipe of larger diameter (25 mm). Since the water in the main pipe is forced through the narrow section, it creates a jet effect.

Media bed technique

Growbeds filled with an inert medium is the most widely used system in small-scale aquaponic systems. This system is strongly recommended in most developing regions because it allows efficient use of space, has a relatively low initial cost and is suitable for beginners because of its simplicity. In growbeds filled with a medium, the inert material is used to support plant roots but also acts as a filter, both mechanical and biological. This dual function is the main reason why such systems are simpler. In the following paragraphs we explain why NFT and DWC methods require specific and more complicated components for filtration. However, the inert filled growbed technique is cumbersome and relatively expensive for large-scale systems. The medium's bed may become clogged if fish stocking densities exceed the loading capacity of the beds and this may require separate filtration. Water evaporation is higher in inert filled beds due to the larger surface area exposed to the sun. Finally, some media are very heavy.

There are many designs for growth beds that use different media, also for this reason it is the technique that is more adaptable to different situations.

Water flow dynamics

The figure shows the main components of an aquaponic system with beds filled with inert material. You can see the fish tank, the growth beds, the pumping sump, as well as the concrete blocks for the support. Reading the drawing is easier to understand, following the flow of water through the system. The water flows by gravity from the fish tank, the beds are filled with porous inert material which also acts as a biofilter.

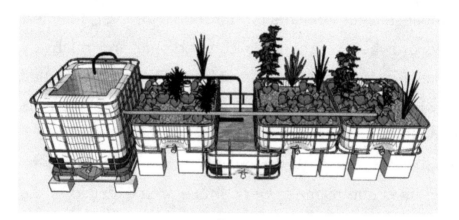

The beds house the colony of nitrifying bacteria and provide a suitable place for plant growth. At the exit of the growbeds, the water continues to the cockpit tank, still by gravity. At this point, the water is relatively free of solid waste in solution and is pumped to the fish reservoir, from where it starts again to the growth beds, resuming the cycle. Some growth beds are designed to get completely wet and then drain, which means that the water level rises at a certain point and then drains completely.

This adds oxygen to the roots of the plants and helps in the biofiltration of ammonia. Other irrigation methods use a constant flow of water, either by feeding it from one side of the bed and leaving the other, or by distributing it through a drip irrigation system.

Construction of a Growbed

We describe how to build an aquaponic plant that is based on the cultivation technology called grow bed.

This is because such a system can be considered among the cheapest, as well as the most suitable for those who are new to aquaponics. However, there are also other cultivation methods used in both aquaponics and hydroponics, using, for example, vertical towers, NFT, and DWC (deep water crops).

The peculiarity of the grow bed system is that the element intended to house the plants, the "growth bed", also acts as a mechanical and biological filter.

Therefore, the elements that constitute an aquaponic system with a growth bed are:

- fish tank
- bed of growth
- sump tub.

To build such a system, first you must make a hole on one of the sides of the fish tank, at a height that will be used to regulate the water level inside the tank. In fact, by means of a pipe that will fish in the lowest part, the water will come out to pour into the "growth bed" positioned on the side, at a slightly lower level.

The "growth bed" must be equipped with a bell-shaped siphon that will allow the continuous filling and emptying of the grow bed.

The growth bed is made up of a container containing inert material which, as already mentioned, guarantees a certain mechanical filtration and allows plant roots and bacteria to anchor and develop. Among the most used and common inert materials, given the low cost and easy availability, there is expanded clay: this substrate, together with the mechanism of the bell siphon, facilitates the oxygenation of plant roots and keeps them anchored.

The water that comes out of the bed through the siphon will be conveyed to the collection tank in which we will place the pump that will bring it back to the fish tank, starting the cycle again.

Once we understand how it works, the possible configurations and experiments are endless, and this is the beauty of it.

Nicolas Campos

CHAPTER 5 - Aquaponics how to make a plant

Aquaponics makes the water filter and plant fertilizer useless, transforming the plant into a self-sufficient mini ecosystem in which waste is recycled from the roots, which filters the water at the same time.

Although no soil and fish farming techniques are very old, the combination of the two is recent and can be traced back to the early 1970s.

Studied all over the world, it is particularly interesting for the reduction of space and costs, for the very low production of organic waste. An ideal activity in schools, it offers educational cues allowing to clarify the concept of biological circle and synergy between living organisms.

The natural union that binds plants, fish and water is evident and obvious, and it is surprising that the relationship was exploited and deepened relatively late.

Fish need a clean, well-oxygenated environment and adequate nutrition.

They produce solid and liquid waste, which if left to accumulate without proper filtration will irreparably pollute the environment and kill the guests.

In our system, the organic waste in question is attacked by nitrifying bacteria.

Plants absorb ammonium and nitrate during the assimilation process, after which they are converted into organic molecules containing nitrogen.

When the nitrogen-based nutrients have fulfilled their function, specialised decomposing bacteria begin a process known as denitrification.

Put simply, during the process plants can absorb the elements they need, while eliminating pollution and providing a healthy environment for fish.

In the Virgin Islands a team of researchers has developed a project to import this technique especially in the archipelagos where most agricultural products must be imported, and the catch is declining.

The University of Davis in California is working on the adaptation of the concept of "family farm". (family farm) providing for the use of aquaponics in the domestic environment for recreational, educational, decorative purposes and to produce biologically on a small to medium scale.

What does it take to start?

- A fish tank and a support for plants
- Bacteria for decomposing fish waste
- A filter to host bacteria and ventilate the tank
- Fish and fish food
- Plants
- pH regulators and tests, micro and macro-element supplements, to make up for any nutritional deficiencies.
- Equipment for plants and fish

You can obtain the tank, the bacteria and the filter to house them from a pet or aquarium product shop. Bacteria do indeed develop naturally within this mini-ecosystem in about 3 weeks, but in order not to take any risks and not to let them run wild for so long it is worth investing in their purchase, also considering that their number can vary and it could be useful to have more of them within reach.

As far as the hydroponic system is concerned, it is possible to choose the type that suits us best: NFT for slower and "soft" growth or aero-hydroponic for dynamic and explosive results, for example.

Oxygenation in this context assumes an essential importance for the correct development of the hosts.

The other determining factors for a good success do not differ much from the traditional ones that are respected in the grow rooms: adequate temperature, cleanliness, good ventilation.

The hydroponic system should simply be positioned above the aquarium and equipped with a pump to create water recirculation.

Fishes

There are several suitable species to choose from.

It is essential that they are cold water fish and not tropical, as they do not like brackish or salt water.

You can buy them all the same or different species; only make sure at the time of purchase that they are compatible breeds and suitable for the size and temperature.

In the greenhouses we have chosen koi carp, a very strong fish of Japanese origin, which can withstand environmental variations well. They are beautiful, colourful, inexpensive animals; although they reach considerable size in the wild, they do not grow much when kept in aquariums.

Plants

You can choose virtually any type of plant.

If it is a commercial plant, a species that thrives in nitrogen-rich environments, such as lettuce or herbs, is preferable.

In fact, it is the food fed to the fish that determines the type of fertilisation of the plants, and there are none commercially available with different amounts of NPK to choose from.

However, if you are an amateur grower, you can venture into the choice of plants according to your personal taste: decorative, edible, medicinal, aromatic and so on.

The important thing is to maintain a balanced ratio between the number of fish and the number of plants to ensure a healthy environment, avoiding toxicity and deficiencies.

Fish nutrition is an important element: it must be of good quality and it is important to make sure that the fish consume it all and do not remain leftovers to decompose in the aquarium.

The best food is live fish. Most fish feed on other fish: it is a very rich and healthy food that forces aquarium guests to chase and catch their prey, an exercise that keeps them healthy and reproduces the natural lifestyle.

It is also possible to produce a balanced food at home following the retailer's instructions; for those who want a 100% organic harvest this is certainly the best choice.

Whatever diet your fish follow, there may be a nutritional deficiency. Quite common is the iron deficiency, which can be made up for by adding a few drops of Bio Essentials (a mix of micro and macro-elements that provides a mixture of iron chelates) every 2 or 3 weeks.

How to start?

First, the aquarium:

- For the well-being of the fish, it is good to put clean aquarium gravel on the bottom.
- Fill the tank slowly with tap water, taking care to put a plastic sheet on the sand in the bottom and a bowl on the plastic: this way the gravel will remain in place.
- Activate the filter and let it turn 24 hours to give time for the chlorine to evaporate (if you don't want to wait buy the special

product in the shop where you bought the fish).

- Important: before introducing the guests, stabilize the pH level at 7, mediating between the acidic environment of 6.5 required by the plants and the slightly basic environment preferred by the fish (7.5).

This operation requires the use of the pH tester and good brand regulators, we use the GHE pH Down powder formula.

It is worth noting that in hydroponics water is usually acidic (5 - 6.5), because it is with these values that plants best assimilate mineral salts. With higher values there is a lowering of the radical absorption capacity, which is why it is recommended to supplement with special products.

- Add the bacteria: two-thirds in the filter, one-third directly on the gravel.

- Add the fish, being careful to choose young specimens that can adapt to the best.

If you have taken them home as you usually do in plastic bags, it is a good idea to leave them about half an hour in their soaking bags in the aquarium, so that they can gradually adapt to the new temperature and have less shock.

- You can now place the plant holders on the tank and fix them securely.
- Now wait 2 - 3 days for the fish to start producing waste and the bacteria to turn it into fertiliser, then introduce the plants.

CHAPTER 6 - How to Make an Aquaponic System at Home

Prepare the Frame

You need the Antonius frame for the main structure. It will consist of one or two baskets and two plastic containers. Use the 50 litres container as a fish tank at the bottom and the 25-litre container for the growth bed at the top. Assemble all parts, based on the relevant package instructions.

Use the basket as a support for the 25-litre plastic container that will house the growth bed. It is not strictly necessary to have the 50-litre plastic container for the fish tank at the base if you just put it on the floor. You should cut the plastic edge of the top container to ensure a better fit; in this tutorial, the handles have also been cut from the end of the container. However, this is not strictly necessary. To cut the plastic, use a small saw or standard wire stripper pliers.

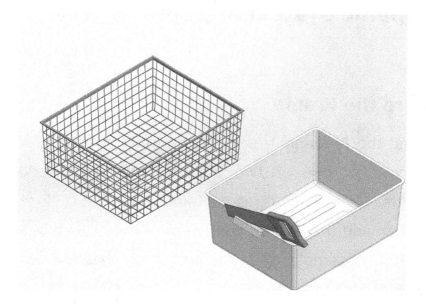

If you want to customize the system to suit the style of your decor, now is the time to do so. The pictures show an example of a fish tank that has been decorated with a strip of PVC.

Hydraulic System

The plumbing for the aquaponic system is not too complicated and you can rely on a few basic principles to help make the system as efficient as possible.

Use a small 600 litres/hour submersible electric pump in a corner of the fish tank that will carry the water to the growth bed. The water flows through the growth bed and out in the opposite corner to the inlet. When the water returns to the fish tank, it pushes any solid waste back to the pump, which will carry it to the growth bed.

Use a by-pass valve in this system. This diverts some of the water from the pump back into the fish tank. This allows you to control the amount of water that will serve the growth bed, while the diverted water creates movement in the fish tank, as well as providing additional ventilation. In this tutorial, 13mm PVC pipes have been used for the entire system. Initially, you should also start with the growth bed and siphon used here.

Get the male and female threaded adapters. Drill a hole in the right place in the growth bed - you need to make sure the female adapter fits into the square of the frame grid. Make the hole about 6 or 7 centimetres from the edge of the housing in each direction; the hole should fit perfectly with the male threaded adapter.

Thread the male adapter through the top of the growth bed. Then mount rubber gaskets on the threads. Then screw the female adapter to the male adapter until a complete, watertight fit is achieved. If you want, but it is not strictly necessary, you can add silicone on the bottom. Finally, use a reducer on top of the male adapter. The one shown here is a reducer from 25mm to 13mm.

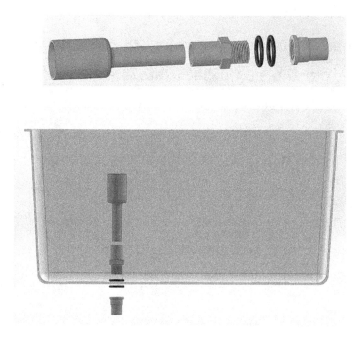

This whole piece is called a standpipe and will allow water to flow out of the growth bed. It is advisable that the overall height is about 2.5 cm below the top of the growth bed; therefore, you will need to cut the tube so that it is at the right height. At this point, let the silicone dry if you have used any.

The Siphon

The bell siphon is a very effective method of slowly flooding the growth bed and then quickly draining the water. And it does this with a non-mechanical action, moreover, it has no moving parts that can break.

Place the 60mm bell siphon in the middle. This is a 60mm piece of pipe with an airtight cap on top. The bell-shaped siphon is shown in the photos with some cut pieces on the bottom, with some holes on the sides - it is advisable that these holes are not higher than about 2.5 cm from the bottom of the tube. The water will drain down to this level and then stop.

Finally, the 100mm protection simply keeps the growth bed material away from the bell siphon. The protection has holes drilled or cut out to allow water to enter - and keep the roots and material out! The cap is optional, but it helps keep things out of the bell siphon.

Bell siphons can be complicated to operate. The mechanics of a siphon trap are relatively complex, but you just need to worry about the practical application of the siphons, so you can quickly empty a growth bed into a tank or fish tank using a simple mechanical method with no electrical or moving parts.

Bypass ball valve

Add a bypass ball valve. This allows you to control how much water flows into the growth bed and is therefore an important addition. The bypass ball valve also allows you to divert water to the fish tank, providing additional aeration and water movement in the tank. This improves fish health.

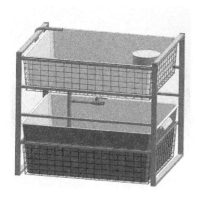 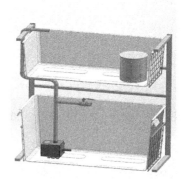

In the pictures shown you can see the small 600 litres/hour pump with a small piece of 13 mm tube inserted. This then has a T-piece attached and continues up to the 90-degree elbow at the top, which brings the water to the growth bed with a 13 mm tube. In the second outlet of the T-piece there is a simple ball valve that controls the flow of water that is diverted back into the fish tank.

Once you have assembled the whole assembly with the frame, containers and plumbing, add water to the fish tank and start the pump. Test to see if everything is working properly and to make sure the system is watertight!

Fill the top container (the growth bed) with some growth material. This could be hydro tonic (aggregate expanded clay pellets), lava stone, perlite, river stones or other similar material. Use something that allows the water to flow through the growth bed and that is not toxic.

Once all this is done, you are ready to add the fish and start putting the plants into the system. Initially, just add a couple of small fish, just to start producing the ammonia needed to start the system.

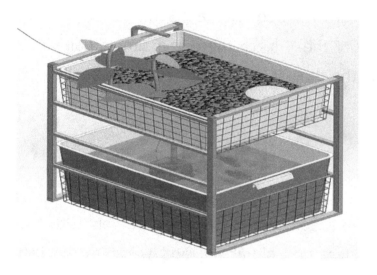

Warnings

Make sure that all pipes are tightly tightened together to prevent leakage. The systems shown in this tutorial are not glued together because a constant push is usually enough!

CHAPTER 7 - Which plants?

To date, more than 150 different vegetables, herbs, flowers and small trees have successfully grown in aquaponic systems, including research, domestic and commercial units. In general, green leafy plants perform very well in aquaponics along with some of the most popular fruit vegetables, including tomatoes, cucumbers and peppers. Fruit and vegetables require more nutrients and are more appropriate in established systems with adequate quantities of fish. However, some tubers and sensitive plants do not grow well in aquaponics. Tubers require special attention, and grow successfully only in medium depth beds, or in a version of breathable beds.

Vegetables vary in relation to their overall nutrient demand. There are two general categories of aquaponic plants based on this demand. Low nutrient demand plants include green leafy vegetables and herbs such as lettuce, thistle, rocket, basil, mint, parsley, coriander, chives, bock choi and watercress. Many legumes such as peas and beans also have a low level of nutrient demand. On the other side of the spectrum are plants with high nutrient demand, sometimes called nutrient hungry. These include fruits such as tomatoes, eggplants, cucumbers, zucchini, strawberries and peppers. Other plants with medium nutrient demand are cabbage, such as cabbage, cauliflower, broccoli and kohlrabi. Bulbous plants such as beets, taro, onions and carrots have an average demand, while radishes require less nutrients.

The growth bed style influences the choice of plants. In medium-bed units, it is common practice to grow polyculture such as green leaves, herbs and fruits at the same time.

By providing medium growth beds at the right depth (at least 30 cm) it is possible to grow all the vegetables mentioned above. Polyculture on small areas can also benefit from complementary plants and better space management, because shade-loving species can grow under taller plants. Mono-crop practices are prevalent in NFT and DWC units because the grower is limited by the number of holes in the pipes and the floats in which to plant the vegetables. Using NFT units, it may be possible to grow vegetables with larger fruits, such as tomatoes, but these plants need plenty of water to ensure an enough supply of nutrients and avoid water stress. Withering in fruit plants can occur almost immediately if the flow is interrupted, with devastating effects on the entire crop. Fruit plants also need to be planted in larger tubes, ideally with flat bottoms, and placed at a greater distance from vegetables and green leaves. This is because fruit plants grow bigger and need more light to ripen and because there is limited space for the roots in the tubes. On the other hand, large bulbs and/or tubers, such as kohlrabi, carrots and turnips, are more likely to be grown in medium beds because NFT and DWC units do not provide a good growing environment and adequate support for the plants. It is important to consider the effects of plant harvesting on the whole ecosystem. If all the plants were collected at once, the result would be an unbalanced system without enough plants to clean the water, resulting in nutrient peaks.

Some farmers use this technique, but it must correspond with a large collection of fish or a reduction in feed intake. However, the recommendation is to use staggered harvesting and a reseeding cycle. The presence of too many plants growing at the same time could result in a system with nutrient deficiency towards the harvest period, when uptake is at its maximum. Having plants at different stages of growth, for example some seedlings and some mature plants, the overall demand for nutrients is always the same. This ensures more stable water chemistry and offers more regular production for both the domestic table and the market.

CHAPTER 8 - Which Fishes in Aquaponics?

If you do not know which fish to use in aquaponics, know that you have many possibilities: from red shrimp to tilapia, from trout to freshwater mussel, up to gilthead sea bream (Sparus aurata) and sea bass (Dicentrarchus labrax), also known as sea bass, two fish for which the possibility of breeding in fresh water has been demonstrated, with lower growth rates than salt water, but managing to maintain the organoleptic characteristics unchanged.

Let's see together in more detail which aquaponic fish to choose and their possible combinations to obtain a multi-trophic plant, depending on whether we are interested in production or just for ornamental purposes.

First of all, it is useful to know that for ornamental species, especially koi, the volume of water available must be taken into account: to keep the fish healthy and ensure adequate growth and good colour development, a high volume is required (at least 1000 litres per koi and 100-150 for goldfish). If we must build a production plant, high fish densities of up to 20 kg/m3 will be required.

We recommend the use of ornamental species for aquaponic systems intended for decorative use or for small domestic production plants (up to 5 thousand litres) as they need a lower mass and density of fish than commercial production plants and this allows to create less stressful conditions for our fish which for this reason will develop their colours in the best way.

Among the ornamental species in aquaculture it is possible to breed koi carp, together with goldfish, sturgeon, gambusia and gobion, as they live together in nature without bothering each other.

Carp koi, gambusie and medaka

We advise you to pay attention to the gambusia, as they are an alien species introduced in the past to fight mosquitoes, but they are very voracious also towards

226

smaller fish, as well as towards eggs and tadpoles, so they can represent a danger if dispersed in the environment.

A very valid alternative to the mosquito is represented by the medaka, also called rice fish or mini-carps koi, which have a much more docile character towards the other species. They originate from Japan, imported into Italy only recently and are similar in size and appearance to gambusia. Moreover, the medaka are very lively fish and do not fear the presence of man, swimming on the surface of the water and giving, thanks to their bright colouring (hence the name of mini koi), a remarkable aesthetic performance and pleasant moments of relaxation.

Feeding: In nature, carp are omnivorous and feed on a wide range of foods, they prefer feeding invertebrates such as: aquatic insects, larvae, worms, molluscs and zooplankton. Some species of grass carp also eat the stems, leaves and seeds of aquatic and terrestrial plants, as well as rotting vegetation.

Reproduction: The best carp fry is obtained from dedicated hatcheries and breeding facilities. The procedure for obtaining fry is more complicated than that used for tilapia, because spawning in female carp is induced by an injection of hormones, a technique that requires a good knowledge of fish physiology and experience.

Gobion, sturgeon and shellfish

As far as the gobion is concerned, it is a very quiet bottom fish compared to other species and needs very low levels of nitrites.

Also, the sturgeon is indicated in an ornamental plant, as it is a fish capable of reaching remarkable dimensions, standing out among the others and becoming in a short time the undisputed protagonist of our body of water.

As far as molluscs are concerned, Planorbarius and Physa marmorata are very suitable, two types of gastropod molluscs that perform an important action, avoiding the accumulation of unconsumed feed, maintaining a cleaner environment and at the same time guaranteeing the complete conversion of the feed not consumed by the fish, so as to optimize the fertilization of the plants. These molluscs also have a further function, they are in fact bio-indicators for the lack of calcium and magnesium carbonates dissolved in water, through the appearance of white lines and deformations of the shell that increase over time.

Fish in Aquaponics for food purposes

Among the most suitable species are Tilapia, redclaw lobster, perch, sun perch, yellow perch, catfish, trout perch and other types of shrimps and molluscs, such as the Anodonta cygnea.

Tilapia

It is one of the most consumed species in the world, in Asia, and lends itself very well to be bred in tanks. In recent years this fish has gained a bad reputation because of the techniques with which it is bred in order to lower costs, i.e. using animal waste instead of feed for the juvenile stage, with the result that its meat is up to 10 times more polluted than wild specimens. We "aquaponists" are convinced that by using a healthy and balanced diet, accompanied by better water quality due to the phyto-purification of plants, the quality and healthiness of this fish can improve considerably compared to the standard on the market.

Nutrition: Tilapies are omnivorous, which means that they have a diet that includes both substances of animal and vegetable origin. They also eat other fish, especially their young; when they are in farming conditions they must be kept separate according to size. While specimens smaller than 15 cm eat smaller fish, when they are larger than 15 cm, they are generally too slow and cease to be a problem for smaller fish.

Reproduction: Tilapias reproduce easily, especially where the water is warm, oxygenated, there is algae, the basin is shaded and the environment calm and peaceful. A rocky substratum on the bottom encourages the construction of the nest. The optimal ratio between males and females is 2 males for every 6-10 females. The fry should be transferred into breeding tanks until the juvenile stages, ensuring that there is no larger fry that could eat them.

Red crayfish (redclaw lobster)

It is a crayfish, particularly suitable in aquaponics in DWC (Deep Water Culture) systems, as its presence helps to keep the roots clean of accumulated organic matter, insects or other small animals. This type of crayfish is successfully grown together with tilapia.

Real perch

It is a fish that lives in both fresh and brackish water, very valuable in the kitchen for its meat and is present in many Italian lakes such as Como and Trasimeno. The perch can reach 60 cm in length and 30 years of age, it is a diurnal and carnivorous fish.

In addition to the royal perch you can also use the trout perch, sun perch and bass "striped bass".

Diet: The trout perch is a carnivorous fish and requires diets rich in protein. They must all be bred the same size to avoid predation of the juveniles by the larger fish.

Aptitude: From a nutritional point of view, trout perch contains relatively high levels of omega-3 fatty acids compared to other freshwater fish.

Anodonta cygnea

Also known as freshwater mussel, it is a bivalve that lives in slow or stagnant watercourses and needs a muddy substrate in which it can establish itself, hiding completely under the sand and thus helping to keep the bottom oxygenated, also avoiding the formation of anoxia zones. The Anodonta cyngea has an enormous filtering capacity that can reach 40 litres per hour, it needs a Ph between 7 and 8, because at lower Ph, the calcium carbonate that makes up its shell begins to melt, quickly leading to the death of the animal: for this reason it is not recommended for the cultivation of strawberries and in general of all those plants that give their best to acid Ph.

This animal feeds on organic matter suspended in the water, but also on protozoa and other microorganisms, many of which are parasites or cause diseases for our fish, accumulating them as a reservoir inside its body. This characteristic represents on the one hand an advantage as it helps to keep the aquatic environment clean and healthy, but at the same time it is good to always keep an eye on freshwater mussels as if they die, in a short time they release all the filtered pollutants, causing significant damage, such as the appearance of diseases or worsening water conditions.

Trout

It is a freshwater fish that lives in streams and mountain lakes, with cold (below 25 degrees) and oxygenated water. There are various types, ranging from rainbow trout, salmon trout, marmorata, up to rainbow trout, the most widespread and resistant even to less oxygenated waters and warmer temperatures.

This last one, compared to the other varieties, is more suitable for the aquaponic cultivation, and considering the commercial value of this fish, we shall soon see many productive plants which will use it.

Nutrition: Trout require a diet richer in proteins than carp and Tilapia, being a carnivorous and not omnivorous species, which means a greater quantity of nitrogen available in the water in relation to the nutrients introduced in the tank.

Suitability: Trout are considered a "fatty fish", with a high amount of vitamin A, vitamin D and omega-3 fatty acids, making them an excellent choice for family consumption.

Sea bass

Also known by the name of sea bass, it is a seawater fish found in all seas, very delicious for its meat. It is a light and digestible fish, with just 97 kcal, 18 grams of protein and 1.7 grams of fat per 100 grams.

It has recently been demonstrated that it can also be reared in brackish and fresh water, managing to maintain its organoleptic characteristics unchanged, but with a drop in growth rates.

It certainly represents a valid choice to make the aquaponic production as sustainable as possible.

Sea bream

It is the seawater fish famous for the golden spot between the eyes and very famous for its lean and tasty meat.

It has a high content of essential amino acids, as well as mostly polyunsaturated and monounsaturated fats. The cholesterol intake is very low, just 65 mg per 100 grams, therefore perfect for low-calorie diets, but also for those suffering from diabetes and obesity.

Recently it has been possible to adapt sea bream to fresh water, thus allowing its use in aquaponics.

Having made some first important distinctions, we will continue in the future to provide you with further advice on which fish you prefer for aquaponics: we too are always looking for new ornamental species and not that can be bred, even in combination.

CONCLUSION

Thank you for making it through to the end of this book, let's hope it was informative and able to provide you with all the tools you need to achieve your goals whatever they may be.

Aquaponics has emerged as a great way to lose growing genuine and tasty vegetable products at home for good health. Yet, many people fail to get all the benefits of this wonderful process due to lack of knowledge of the process. This book has tried to bring all the important points to the fore so that you can get all the benefits of aquaponic without having to deal with the negative effects.

All you must do is follow the information provided in the book and follow the directions.

You can also get all the benefits of the process by following the simple steps in the book.

I hope that this book will really help you achieve your goals.

AEROPONICS

The Beginner's Guide to Growing your Own Organic Fruit Vegetable and Ornamental Plants Garden at Home

Nicolas Campos

INTODUCTION

Aeroponics is the method of growing crops above ground using nebulizers. The good thing is that the entire cultivation process is highly automated, but still requires very strict management.

The availability of lighting is also an important component in agricultural production. Adequate lighting is achieved by planting crops in vertical structures to maximize accessibility to light, while density and shading are kept to a minimum.

These growing conditions for plant cultivation, in terms of water, nutrients and light, are ideal for crops and maximise the usefulness of the growing area and use the space that might otherwise be unused. Having a mobile multi-level growing structure exposes the plants to ideal lighting during the growing season.

Nicolas Campos

CHAPTER 1 - What is Aeroponics Growing?

Aeroponics is an indoor growing system, in a greenhouse or inside a grow box, where plants are grown without the use of soil, thanks to special systems characterized by a supporting structure, mesh pots in which plants are placed, nutritive solutions based on water and mineral fertilizers and air pumps. These are used to atomise the liquid solution, which - thanks to the action of the air - can reach the roots of the plants and nourish them in depth. Thanks to the aeroponic technique, it is possible to obtain ideal conditions for the development of plants. On the one hand, the closed and isolated environment will make cultivated plants much less susceptible to attacks from fungi and diseases, on the other hand, the roots will have a high level of oxygenation and can thus grow quickly with a minimum amount of water and mineral salts. Unlike in hydroponic cultivation, the plant is not irrigated - in the traditional sense of the term - with nutrients but suspended in a mesh pot from which the roots will come out, which will be periodically sprayed with nutrients. This system allows to consume even less water than what is usually used in a hydroponic cultivation system, because it is recovered and put back into the circuit thanks to a recovery system. Aeroponics is particularly suitable for all those crops that can develop vertically - thus avoiding contributing to soil exploitation - and less so for crops that need ample space, such as wheat and corn.

In an aeroponic system the plants develop outside the soil, they are continuously irrigated with the nebulization system, thanks to an immersion pump, in a completely controlled environment where the presence and spread of parasites and diseases, typical of soil cultivation, is very difficult.

Thanks to the constant and precise monitoring (with special instruments) of the fundamental environmental parameters (lighting, nutrition, temperature, humidity, pH and conductivity), it is possible to obtain significantly better results than normal cultivation in soil. All this without having to use - as in traditional crops -

insecticides and pesticides that are potentially harmful to human and plant health (and with the relative consequences for the environment).

We would also like to remind you that the indoor cultivation technique using the aeroponic method allows to obtain extraordinary results in terms of speed and quantity, but also in quality.

But let's take a closer look, before referring you to the next chapters of this guide, at how - specifically - aeroponic cultivation works.

In this type of cultivation, the plants are placed in a system of PVC conduits - suitable for this type of cultivation - and installed at the top, supported by special panels, so that they remain suspended. At the base of these plastic conduit's nebulizers are placed, which will have the task of nebulizing the nutritive solution to the plants. The do-it-yourself aeroponic culture - which identifies a method but also a completely different way of growing, so much so that it is also called "aeroponic culture" - makes it possible to irrigate and feed the plants, making them grow healthy, without using chemicals and with a great saving of water. With all that this means for the health of our environment. It is no coincidence that the number of aeroponic cultivation in the world is constantly growing, so much so that there is an increase in aeroponic greenhouses.

In the water - which is sprayed with a special pump provided by the aeroponic system - all the essential nutrients to feed the cultivated plants are dissolved. The growth time of the plants is generally reduced compared to the growth and development time of plants grown in soil with traditional systems.

CHAPTER 2 – How to Start an Aeroponic Growing?

In order to be able to start cultivating with the aeroponic methods, it is necessary first to have all the necessary tools in the three phases of growth and development of the plant: the germination period, the growth period and, finally, the flowering phase.

Once you have studied all the phases and learned all the tricks to be able to grow indoors using the aeroponics method, you must have all the appropriate tools.

For the Germination Phase:

Necessary

- Mini greenhouse (to germinate seeds)
- Rockwool cubes (at least 1 per seed to germinate)
- Root stimulator

Optional

- Neon Light

- Watertight heating resistor (to keep the temperature of the mini- greenhouse stable at the optimum temperature of about 26 degrees).

For the Growth and Flowering Phase:

Necessary

- Indoor Lighting Kit (in chapter 4 we will explain how to choose the lighting system)
- Bulb/bulb
- Power supply
- Lamp/reflector holder
- Aeroponic system
- pH Meter/Test
- EC Meter/Test
- PH corrector
- Nutrients for the growth phase
- Nutrients for the flowering phase
- Timer for timing

Optional

- Thermometer/hygrometer
- Grow box / Grow Room or Mylar Cloth
- Get on and off (easy roller)
- Humidifier
- Fan

To set up the environment for the germination phase, the first and for some aspects the most important, it is necessary to get some rockwool cubes and the rootbooster, that is a product that - thanks to its composition - is able to stimulate and accelerate the development of the roots, strengthening them compared to a normal root system of a plant grown in soil.

How to prepare the germination

Combine 5 litres of water and 20 ml of a very powerful root development stimulator, which has the function of stimulating the growth of the root system.

With the liquid prepared, soak the rockwool cubes and leave them for about 24 hours to adjust their pH (which tends upwards, about 7.0).

The next day, remove the cubes from their solution and drain them well, so that the excess water comes out and oxygen enters, thus ensuring an adequate exchange of water and air.

push the seed to be grown into the hole inside the cube, to a depth of about half a centimetre.

Place the rockwool cubes in the mini- greenhouse you have purchased (or built according to the recommended criteria) and make sure that the temperature and humidity parameters are ideal for this phase: 26° with a high level of humidity (about 80%).

Place the neon lamp and keep it on all day (24 hours a day).

In the initial germination phase, the seed inserted in the stone wool cube does not need light, while it begins to need the action of the lamps when it starts to sprout and come out of the cube: it is essential to illuminate with a light that is not strong (preferably neon) or with special

HPS and/or MH lamps, provided that the level of temperature and humidity is always checked.

If the plants do not receive adequate lighting, they will develop a much longer stem than normal. It can be said that the period needed to see the seed germinate is a minimum of two days and a maximum of two weeks. Remember not to touch the seed once it has been inserted and placed in the stone wool cube. Once the seed has developed, you will be able to see the roots that will cross the cube at the sides and bottom of the stone wool support.

If you want to use the propagation method for cuttings, we recommend this type of product: x-stream propagators of nutri cultures.

How to germinate seeds in rockwool cubes

Insert the seed into the hole (of the cube 4x4cm) at a depth of about 2cm.

At this point, it is necessary to cover and protect the cube inside a mini greenhouse or other container that can ensure that the temperature is kept around 26 and the humidity is high, about 80%.

The roots - once through the cube - will tend to come out from the sides and bottom of the cube. Depending on the use, the 4x4cm cube, once germinated, can also be inserted into the 7.5x7.5cm cube which has a 4x4cm hole on the top side (suitable for the smaller cube).

Once this first phase - i.e. the germination period - has been completed, the rockwool cubes can be used in any substrate (e.g. soil or coconut fibre) in hydroponic systems (clay, lapilli, perlite), or placed on NFT trays (i.e. a technique called Nutrient Film Technique that does not require the presence of the substrate).

The seed initially requires no light. Once the seedling comes out of the cube, however, it is essential to light it with gentle light (preferably with a neon light at a distance of about 1 cm) or an HPS and/or MH lamp (always monitoring both temperature and humidity).

Always remember that seedlings that do not receive adequate light tend to have a very long stem. Depending on the type, quality and age of the seeds, germination can take from 2 days to a maximum of 14 days. Always remember that the seed during germination is very delicate and should not be touched.

CHAPTER 3 - Step-by-step Installation

When the seed will have opened, thus ending the first phase of growth of the plant, it is essential to set up the aeroponic system in which to insert the cube of wool and the seed just germinated.

Today, on the market, there are many different aeroponic systems, but - in this specific case - we will take as reference and example the Amazon aeroponic system by Nutriculture, one of the most appreciated and sold, which is characterized by its advanced technology and the great results it is able to guarantee.

In any case, it is possible to use other systems; in this case it is advisable to follow the instructions provided by the manufacturer itself in the manual present in the product packaging.

How to set up the aeroponic system:

- fix the lower tank;

- put the pump inside the tank.
- place the upper tank;
- place over the perforated cover.
- connect the pump to the main connection and sprinklers.
- place the pots on the upper tank.
- connect the pump to the timer and to the mains.
- fill the tank with water and fertiliser (down a dedicated chapter).
- place the cube, with all the bud, in its pot.

Lighting Installation

At this point, it is necessary to illuminate the plant as soon as it comes out of the germination period: it is necessary to provide a lighting system to make the bud grow and bloom as if it were illuminated by natural sunlight.

A lighting system for aeroponic cultivation will consist of:

1. Power supply (or Ballast) to give an enough and pulse of current to turn the lamp on. Electronic

ballasts - compared to ferromagnetic ones - have the advantage of:

- consume less power.
- heat a little.
- be more stable and durable.
- make wiring easier.
- adjust the watts on some models.

2. Bulb (or bulb) to simulate the effect of the sun. There are various types of bulbs on the market for aeroponic cultivation. The difference is in the technology used and in the different spectrum of light and colours. Remember that for vegetative growth you need a light spectrum tending to blue (MH lamps), while for flowering you need a light spectrum tending to orange/red (HPS lamps). Agriculture lamps are those that can be used in both growth and flowering phases (for this reason they are often recommended, because they are more comfortable and easier to manage).

3. Lamp holder and Reflector to support the bulb and diffuse the light - correctly and evenly - throughout the aeroponic growing area. Also, for this type of

product there are various types on the market, but - in general - it is good to know that the two fundamental types of reflectors are air cooled and traditional ones (not air cooled).

In the table you can find a summary in order to find the right lighting system starting both from the cultivation space available (i.e. the size of the grow box or grow room) and from the number of plants grown inside it.

	150 Watt	250 Watt	400 Watt	600 Watt	1000 Watt
Plants number	1/2	2/4	3/6	4/10	8/18
m2	0.5	0.75	1	1.4	1.5
Grow room/ Box	70x70x 180	80x80x 180	100x100x 200	120x120x 200	240x120x 200

Connect the power supply to the mains.

Electronic power supplies are simpler and more immediate to use, because they already have the connection to the electrical network ready, ferromagnetic ones are more complicated, because they must be wired manually.

Connect the ballast to the lamp/reflector holder.

The lamp holder to connect the ballast to the lamp is always equipped with a standard socket, called E40.

The lamp/reflector holder reflects and diffuses the light from the lamp. It is usually supplied with the entire lamp holder kit.

Screw the bulb to the lamp holder once wired, you must screw the bulb to the lamp holder and clean the bulb with a clean, dry cloth before turning it on.

Cultivation LED

The LED for cultivation can be used to grow any type of plant at any stage of development. The emission of white and red simulates the colour gradation on the orange tone, like an agriculture lamp.

The led has a higher cost than other products, but it has some advantages, such as current saving and the fact that it doesn't heat up; moreover, it is easy to mount and doesn't need power supplies and other supports.

Grow Room

A grow room is a growing area for indoor growing, even with the aeroponic system. You can grow indoors in any enclosed space, but you need to take several factors into account to ensure that all the parameters useful for the growth of the plant are regularly monitored and controlled to achieve the best possible result.

Here are the basic parameters to be monitored inside the grow box for indoor aeroponic growing:

- The light
- The temperature
- Humidity

- Ventilation, ventilation and carbon dioxide (CO2)

Light

The hours of light - and more generally the lighting in indoor aeroponic cultivation - is one of the most important factors because it is particularly decisive for the health and growth of plants.

Plants need the correct amount of light in order to simulate sunlight and feed the cultivated plants correctly.

The first step to take, in order to correctly manage and dose the hours and quantities of light, is to isolate the growing environment (for this reason it is recommended to use a grow box or set up a grow room correctly) in order to prevent the sun's rays from penetrating inside, a factor that will allow you to completely manage the artificial light and monitor it correctly. The presence of reflective mylar sheets inside the grow box or grow room will facilitate the uniform propagation of light within the growing area and will correctly illuminate the plants.

During the growing phase it is necessary to provide the plant with about 18 hours of light per day. In the third or fourth week of the growing phase it is possible to reduce the light hours from 18 to 12 hours: the plant will feel the arrival of autumn (thus simulating shorter light days) and will start flowering before winter arrives. In any case, it is not recommended to let the plant bloom when it is still too small and weak, as the structure and stem would not be able to support many flowers.

The timer is an indispensable tool for planning and activating the switching on and off lights within the indoor aeroponic growing area. There are many types of timers, from the most essential ones from a few euros to the more advanced ones, which cost of course a little more, but allow several additional features and definitely very useful. Among the cheap ones we find the analogy timers that allow you to plan within 24 hours but have limitations. There are also digital timers that allow more detailed programming.

Temperature

Among the basic parameters to be monitored within an indoor aeroponic cultivation area is the temperature (as in all indoor cultivation). The ideal temperature is between 21 and 28 degrees centigrade and you can monitor it with special precision instruments, such as thermometers or thermo hygrometers. Among the thermometers recommended to monitor the temperature of the grow box, there is definitely the digital one, with the minimum and maximum function, which allows you to check the temperature at any time of the day to verify the minimum and maximum temperature reached by the environment during the 24 hours. In this way it is possible to know the anomalies and run to the shelters.

But what should we do if the thermometer used indicates that the temperature is excessive? To lower the temperature inside a grow room it is possible to use a special vacuum cleaner or air extractor that sucks in the hot air in the room to push it outside, thus cooling the air in the grow room. The fan can be operated with a thermostat, so that it only works during the hottest hours, when the lamps are on.

If this doesn't lower the temperature either, you can think of an air conditioner.

What if the temperature is too low? To raise it, you can use an electric stove that can be adjusted and operated by a thermostat.

Humidity

Among the parameters to be constantly monitored there is of course - as mentioned above - also humidity, which is fundamental to ascertain the state of health and the correct development of plants grown indoors using aeroponic methods.

The humidity should be around 50-60%. To measure it correctly you should use a hygrometer, because if the humidity levels rise too high, you run the risk of mould, which causes damage to the plants.

If the humidity level should rise too high, it is advisable to use an air extractor (sucking in hot air also lowers the humidity). If the humidity level is too low, it is advisable to use a humidifier for the grow room.

Ventilation, ventilation and carbon dioxide

The movement, intake and extraction of air from an environment is one of the most important aspects of a hydroponic system and - more generally - in indoor plant cultivation, which is often not sufficiently taken into account when deciding to set up and start a new project.

Providing proper ventilation for your growing area is essential and vital for your greenhouse or environment, more commonly called a grow room. Adequate ventilation - and therefore proper air recirculation - inside the grow box is important for many reasons: temperature control, humidity, disease, odour control and air recirculation, which ensures a continuous exchange between the entry of fresh air and the exit of stale air.

Providing fresh air to the growing environment increases the amount of CO2, which is essential for the survival and health of all plants. CO2, in fact, represents about 50% of the dry weight of the plant, with oxygen accounting for the remaining 42%.

NOTE: Always remember that plants require CO2 to grow healthily and - in the absence of this - the consequences are harmful.

You need to know that plants - within any hydroponics and indoor growing - will absorb the available carbon dioxide in a very short time, so it is essential to provide them with clean, fresh air to maintain adequate CO2 levels and prevent them from dropping, which would greatly reduce the yield of the crop. Having small amounts of CO2 results in slow growing crops and poor yields.

As well as increasing CO_2 levels, ensuring proper air circulation in your grow box - providing fresh air and allowing stale air to escape - reduces the risk of diseases developing in your greenhouse. It is good to remember that humid, stale air endangers the health of your plants.

It is no coincidence that diseases normally develop in environments where the air is still and humid, a situation that favours the development of dangerous diseases, dictated by the high level of humidity and the lack of air recirculation. If this aspect is not controlled and managed correctly, through a special ventilation for indoor environments, plants will tend to lose vigour and wither progressively.

In addition to what has already been seen, proper air recirculation inside the grow room or grow box - or greenhouse - is also essential to avoid the appearance and proliferation of insects, which normally cause serious damage to plants.

One way to minimize insect damage is to install a fan - fixed or rotating - dedicated to fresh air recirculation.

In essence, an efficient air recirculation system will provide plants with the correct level of carbon dioxide, allowing the development of strong, healthy roots that can absorb the necessary amounts of water and nutrients and - at the same time - minimize the damage caused by diseases and insects.

It should be remembered that the type and model of the ventilation system chosen for your hydroponic cultivation is a real priority in order to ensure abundant and quality harvests. The calculation that is made to identify the most suitable ventilation system for your growing area may be complex and require many variables. So, let's make it clearer and simpler by providing the key elements to identify the most suitable system. It should of course be borne in mind that, in general, the larger the cultivation environment, the more powerful the indoor ventilation system will have to be. Usually, two light grow rooms are used, but to know what kind of ventilation your plants need, it is essential to make some calculations.

Ventilation

The first thing to do - in order to find the right ventilation for your indoor cultivation - is to accurately measure the volume of your greenhouse - or your growing area - in cubic metres.

Once you have measured the length, width and height of your grow room, simply use the following formula to get the total cubic meters, the size of your room.

Length X Width X Height= Greenhouse volume in m2.

Let's make a practical example and assume that your greenhouse has the following dimensions: length: 3.65 meters, width 2.4 meters and height 2.5 meters.

multiplying these three values (3.65 X 2.4 X 2.5), the result will be 21.9 cubic metres.

On the other hand, it is good to remember that the more isolated the grow room, the better. A well-insulated environment will be easier to manage on an environmental level.

Below you will find a very simple tool to automatically calculate the flow rate of the ideal ventilation system for your greenhouse, depending on the parameters you need to enter.

The ventilation in the grow room and in general the recirculation of air is - as we have seen - a factor of primary importance. As written above - and in the other guides - good ventilation allows your grow air to avoid humidity accumulation and temperature rise.

The process of air extraction becomes, therefore, an indispensable element whose objective is the extraction of indoor air so that all the air is extracted every 4/6 minutes. An extraction system consists of the following elements:

- The extractor to extract the air from the grow box
- The extraction pipe or hose
- The fan for fresh air supply
- A fan (optional to improve air recirculation)
- An activated carbon filter (optional to eliminate odours at the outlet)

Aspirator

An air extractor must be chosen primarily according to the flow rate. To do the calculation, multiply the volume of the grow room (or grow box) by 75. To select the most suitable type of extractor you must multiply

Height x Width x Depth x 75 = Air extractor flow rate.

Once the flow rate has been calculated, you can select the recommended model for the growing space (grow box, grow room or greenhouse). You will then necessarily also need to buy the ducts - check the diameter - or choose the necessary reducers. To connect the extractor to the pipe/pipeline, use special connecting strips or resistant adhesive tape. Also, in this case, a timer should be used to adjust the control units and thus control the temperature and humidity levels.

Carbon dioxide (CO2) in the grow room

As mentioned above, when growing in a closed environment, there is a risk that the plants - when growing - consume a lot of carbon dioxide (CO2); if this happens, the growth of the plant will slow down considerably. In order to maintain high levels of Co2 it will be enough to let air from outside into the grow room with the help of an extractor. Often, however, excessive air recirculation causes the temperature to drop too low. In this case, it is possible to forcibly dispense carbon dioxide with the help of a CO2 cylinder dispenser.

CHAPTER 4 – Irrigation, Conductivity and Fertilization of the Aeroponic System

Irrigation is of course another extremely important aspect for the health and growth of plants in an aeroponic crop, because through irrigation - in addition to providing the necessary water - it also provides the necessary nutrients for the plant.

Therefore, it is essential to ensure water quality and control the two main parameters: pH and conductivity/Ec (electrical conductivity).

The pH must be between 5.8 - 6.0: with a pH meter you can see if the solution is acidic or basic.

If the solution is too acidic, it will have to be corrected with pH+, if the water is too basic, it will have to be corrected with pH-.

pH- with 30% phosphoric acid to lower the pH value of the nutrient solution.

pH + with Potassium carbonate to increase the pH value in the growth and flowering phase.

The electrical conductivity (EC) is measured in mS/sec milli-Siemens per second with a special instrument, the conductivity meter. The measurement of this value is essential because it identifies the amount of salts dissolved in the water.

The salts naturally present in tap water generally vary from zone to zone, so it is recommended to use osmotic water or water filtered with a special reverse osmosis system. In this way the water values bring the electrical conductivity close to zero.

The recommended conductivity values change between germination and growth/flowering phases.

In the germination phase the Ec should be between 0.6 and 1.0.

In the growth and flowering phases between 1.0 and 2.0.

In the last flowering phase, it is advisable to go down as in the first phase, between 0.6 and 1.0.

When the electrical conductivity is too low you need to increase the amount of fertilizer, if it is too high you need to decrease the fertilizer.

Water temperature is another important factor in hydroponic and aeroponic cultivation: it should be between 15 and 23 degrees centigrade.

Fertilisers and nutrients are crucial for plants in indoor growing because - unlike plants in soil - those grown on substrates other than soil need to take their nutrients elsewhere.

There are so many types on the market, the important thing is to make sure that the ones we want to use are designed - and therefore suitable - for plants grown in aeroponics and hydroponics.

Below are the doses and how to use the fertilizers to be used during the growth and flowering phases.

In the diagram Cellmax products are used (in case you decide to use another brand it is advisable to follow the instructions on the package): in the summary below are indicated the various weeks, the products and the doses to be administered.

- CellMax Rootbooster 0.5L
- CellMax HYDRO Grow 2x1L
- CellMax HYDRO Bloom 2x1L
- Cellmax Superenzyme 0.5L
- Cellmax P-K Booster 1L

CHAPTER 5 - Hydroponics vs Aeroponics

Hydroponics and aeroponics are both extremely efficient techniques for the cultivation of plants without the use of soil and, therefore, allow to cultivate everywhere, even where there is no soil.

They can be applied both indoors (indoor growing) and outdoors (if the right climatic conditions are in place) and all that is needed to grow the plants is to develop a nutrient solution based on water and nutrients. Even better if the irrigation and feeding process of the plants is managed through an automatic system, so that the continuous intervention of a person in charge is required.

Hydroponics: specific characteristics

In hydroponic cultivation - as already discussed in our guides, manuals and blog articles - plants are grown without soil and with the use of water. Actually, it is good to know that there are different types of hydroponic systems, which use different structures and elements, but - in general - it is possible to say that with this technique plants grow thanks to the action of water enriched with nutrients. In a first period, the plants are started inside inert substrates, such as coconut fibre, perlite, expanded clay, or other materials useful for the realization of substrates, and then pass inside hydroponic systems, which provide - in addition to water supply - also a proper lighting, thanks to the presence of ad hoc lamps, temperature, humidity and proper ventilation of the environment.

Aeroponics: specific characteristics

Aeroponics is an alternative form of cultivation of plants, vegetables and fruits that does not require the use of soil or water.

With this cultivation technique, in fact, plants live and grow brilliantly and healthily thanks to the nebulization of a nutritive solution, based on water and substances useful for growth, which are delivered to the roots with a special sprayer. This technique should not be confused with hydroponics, where the most important element is not air - as in this case - but water.

Once the aeroponic system is set up, the plants are suspended with the roots in the air inside a grow room (or cultivation chamber) where they will remain until harvesting time.

Underlying the growth and health of the plants is certainly the constant control of temperature, humidity and lighting.

Pros and Cons of Hydroponics

The advantages of using a hydroponic system are certainly the reduced maintenance, the possibility to grow at any time of the year and the opportunity to control the climate of the growing environment.

More generally, the great advantage of hydroponics is in complete control over nutrients and, therefore, plant growth. In addition, hydroponically grown plants have a better yield than plants grown in soil. Many such systems recycle water and reduce waste.

In fact, these soil-free growing systems use only 10% of the amount of water needed for conventional crops and are easy to build and assemble. Hydroponic gardens do not require the use of herbicides or pesticides, precisely because no weeds grow there, they need little space and are not dependent on the growing seasons, because they use lamp light, which can be installed anywhere.

However, hydroponic gardens have drawbacks; for example, if the temperature is too high or too low, even for just one day, plants could die or suffer serious damage. In addition, the purchase of hydroponic systems and accessories may be expensive, especially if you are not an expert.

Pros and Cons of Aeroponics

Among the advantages of aeroponics is - in absolute first place - the efficiency and cleanliness of the growing environment.

With this technique, in fact, you get excellent and flourishing harvests in a short period of time. Another important advantage is the very low risk of contracting diseases and bacterial infections. On the other hand, a disadvantage - especially if you are a beginner - lies in the rather high cost, because it requires the purchase of a series of equipment. In addition, you need a dedicated indoor room in which you can install the aeroponic system.

Hydroponics and Aeroponics: Similarities and Differences

Hydroponics and aeroponics have a lot in common: aeroponics are - in fact - a hydroponics culture, which also uses the benefits of air. To simplify and summarize, we can say that aeroponics is an evolution of hydroponics, to get the most out of the potential of plants in terms of yield and speed.

The main difference between the two techniques is that hydroponic systems come in many forms: plants can be suspended in water full-time, or they can be fed by a continuous or intermittent flow. In a hydroponic system, plants grow with water and without soil, with the help of inert substrates. The two systems have in common the supply of nutrients that are delivered directly from the source and supplied to the roots.

Plants in aeroponics, on the other hand, are never put into water, but are sprayed remotely thanks to a dispenser that hydrates and nourishes the roots several times an hour, thanks to an automated system that guarantees their regularity and punctuality. One reason why these two cultivation methods have so much in common is that aeroponics is a type of hydroponic cultivation. The main difference is that hydroponic systems can be of various types: there are different types and for this reason you can choose the one that best suits your needs.

A common disadvantage of both hydroponic and aeroponic growing systems is that - relying on automated systems that require electricity - they may require the use of expensive generators, which can be used in the event of power outages. However, once set up and started up, hydroponics and aeroponic systems can make significant savings compared to traditional growing techniques.

According to current phenomena, it is possible that forms of hydroponic and aeroponic agriculture will increase in popularity over time and become commonplace in the homes of all of us. It is certain that - due to climate change and the unregulated action of man - the amount of soil available for cultivation will tend to decrease and its quality will continue to deteriorate, so more and more people will try to produce healthy food in their homes (many have already started growing salads, tomatoes, strawberries, etc.). Hydroponic and aeroponic gardens and gardens can provide the right answer to these growing needs.

Nicolas Campos

284

Nicolas Campos

CHAPTER 6 – Which Plants to Grow

Aeroponic cultivation is becoming increasingly popular. Due to its ability to adapt to many different situations such as the absence of green space or unfavourable weather, more and more space is being made available for cultivation, becoming the preferred solution for many.

The ecosystem that is created inside a grow box can offer the plant everything it needs to be able to grow luxuriant and healthy. All plants grown indoors, in fact, are grown without the use of pesticides. A great benefit that eliminates the risk of water, air and soil pollution.

Not all plants, however, are easy to grow at home: succulent plants, for example, need a drier soil as do some bulb plants. So, let's see which plants are best suited for aeroponic cultivation, which you can start growing at home right away.

7 Ideas on Which Plants to Grow Indoors Directly at Home

Light Cannabis

The most cultivated plant in indoor aeroponics is certainly the legal hemp: with this cultivation system it will be possible to obtain even 4 or 5 harvests per year, optimizing the production to the maximum.

To start the cultivation of hemp, it is essential to choose only and only seeds certified at European level. Growing it indoors always allows you to produce it non-stop and have a controlled product in every aspect and always of the same high quality.

To learn more about how to grow medical cannabis legally.

Microgreens

Considered by many to be the food of the future, microgreens or micro-gifts are very young small plants of different types of vegetables that are perfect for indoor aeroponic cultivation. They are harvested at a more advanced stage of ripeness than sprouts.

It is possible to grow them without the need for specific agricultural knowledge, they are suitable for all seasons and with the help of LED lamps they grow strong and fresh. Ideally, they should be harvested after a period of 7 to 20 days after sowing. Rich in vitamins and minerals, they are perfect in the kitchen, so much so that even great chefs often use them.

Peppers

Another perfect vegetable for aeroponic cultivation is pepper. With all its bright colours, this vegetable can be grown at home for a steady harvest and full of vitamin C and antioxidant properties.

With the use of a grow room, in fact, you can recreate the ideal environment for these plants to grow strong and tasty. With the use of LED lamps, you will be able to have pepper on your table all year round, not only in summer as it normally happens, and with all its organoleptic characteristics intact.

Tomatoes

The most common product in aeroponic cultivation after hemp is certainly the tomato, a great protagonist of the Mediterranean diet. With this type of cultivation, you don't have to wait for the right season, but you can enjoy the fresh taste of the tomato whenever you want, to put in salad or to make preserves.

According to recent studies, moreover, tomatoes grown indoors with the help of LED lights seem to grow richer in nutrients than normal vegetables grown in the garden or vegetable garden. Compared to sunlight alone, LED bulbs, if properly adjusted, can reach certain points on the plant otherwise hidden, thus exploiting all the potential it offers.

Decorative plants

Ornamental plants embellish the house and in an aeroponic cultivation they can grow more and more beautiful and dense. In this case green leafy plants such as Ficus or pothos are ideal. They are easy to grow indoors and very ornamental.

Aromatic plants

Another idea for aeroponic cultivation is to choose aromatic plants, which will fill the nostrils and dishes of your kitchen with their good smell. Basil, rosemary, parsley: choose the herbs you prefer and start your cultivation. It will be enough to keep under control especially temperature and humidity to always have with you your favorite aromas.

Orchids

Finally, the delicacy of orchids finds a perfect environment in aeroponic cultivation. Even those who have fewer green thumbs will be able to grow this beautiful flower at home in all its different species. Among these, epiphytic and terrestrial orchids are particularly suitable.

Growing them at home is an excellent solution, which allows you to stem some problems that might otherwise occur in the presence of soil and increase the quality of the plant itself.

CONCLUSION

Thank you for coming all the way to the end of this book, we hope it has been informative and able to provide you with all the tools you need to achieve your goals, whatever they may be.

Aeroponics has emerged as a great way to achieve the growing of genuine and tasty plant products at home for good health. Yet, many people fail to get all the benefits of this wonderful process due to lack of knowledge of the process. This book has tried to bring all the important points to the fore so that you can get all the benefits of aeroponics without having to deal with the negative effects.

All you must do is follow the information provided in the book and follow the directions.

You can also get all the benefits of the process by following the simple steps in the book.

I hope this book will really help you achieve your goals.

Nicolas Campos

Nicolas Campos

GREENHOUSE GARDENING

A Complete Beginner's Guide to Growing Organic Vegetables and Fruits. Learn How to Build and Maintain your Own Greenhouse and Hoophouse, DIY

Nicolas Campos

INTRODUCTION

This book is designed specifically for those who want to build their own greenhouse and grow their own 100% organic vegetables and fruits to eat healthily and benefit their health.

Greenhouse cultivation is part of the concept of protected cultivation.

Would you like to learn more about this branch of agriculture and how to create a greenhouse?

The forms of cultivation in which means are used to protect plants from adverse climatic factors, which could affect their normal development, are called protected crops.

Protected crops include horticulture, floriculture, nursery and fruit-growing.

The means of protection include a very wide range of structures, which may differ:

Complexity: from simple ground cover to the most modern and complex greenhouses equipped with air conditioning systems.

For the duration of their use in relation to the cultivation cycle: i.e. the protection can be used for the entire cultivation period or only part of it.

With the use of the greenhouse it is possible:

- Realize a different degree of climate control.
- Cultivate certain species in environments other than those of origin where they can grow naturally (e.g. ornamental species of tropical origin cultivated in our environments).
- Anticipate or delay production compared to the normal period (semi-fortification).
- To realize productions completely out of season (forcing).

To obtain the forcing we use stable greenhouses: practicable structures equipped with glass or plastic covers and used for the whole cycle.

For the cultivation of plants in a sub-optimal environment and for semi-forced production, simpler means of protection such as agro-textiles or tunnels are enough.

The purpose of this book is particularly aimed at those who want to cultivate natural organic products at any time of the year both professionally and amateurishly.

This book will not only explain how to build your greenhouse but will also explain in detail which plants you can produce in your greenhouse, when to sow, how to maintain and care for the greenhouse and the plants to obtain excellent natural products.

This book will explain the complete processes and reasons for doing things in the specific ways that are recommended. It will give you a thorough understanding of the whole process from sowing to harvesting.

This book is a sincere attempt to help you understand the principles of greenhouse cultivation and the ways in which it can help you get genuine products and improve your health.

I hope you will be able to take full advantage of this book.

There are many books on this topic on the market, thank you again for choosing this one! Every effort has been made to ensure that it is full of as much useful information as possible; enjoy it!

CHAPTER 1 - Greenhouse Types

When it comes to greenhouses, our mind almost always runs fast to the intensively cultivated fields. An image that doesn't really coincide entirely with what greenhouses are. A greenhouse, in fact, is an artificial environment that contributes to the growth of plants in environments not congenial to their cultivation. When we talk about plants, of course, we are not only referring to fruit plants or vegetables, but also to flowers. In this sense, there are numerous possibilities of application, which often have distant origins.

A brief historical note

The story of the greenhouses, in fact, starts from afar. The idea of growing in a protected environment spread when the passion for tropical plants was born, especially in northern countries. At that point it was necessary to identify systems that would allow plants to survive even in environments that were not congenial to their growth. According to some, already in the fifteenth century the first systems, such as the matted pavilions that allowed the growth of such plants, spread.

In the following centuries the passion for exotic plants and the spread of greenhouses grew in parallel. Already in the 18th century, in fact, you can recognize the first real greenhouses: not yet in the form to which we are accustomed today, but as buildings with large glass surfaces and colonnades to support them. The use of greenhouses, up to that point, was not limited only to the growth of plants. Greenhouses were, on the contrary, places to spend time and, for this purpose, were set up for banquets and dances.

With technological progress, iron replaced masonry colonnades. Thus, were born the winter gardens, which continued to be ornament of villas and palaces. Here too, however, the greenhouses have retained their function as halls to host parties. At the same time, however, the first experimental gardens became widespread, where plants that usually grow far away could be studied closely. From here to the use of greenhouses in cultivation, as we are used to nowadays, the step was short.

Types of greenhouses

The criteria for classifying greenhouse types are different. Essentially the different types of greenhouses can be grouped according to the function for which they are intended. In this case we can have:

- **multiplication greenhouses** (also called propagation greenhouses): they are greenhouses mainly used to promote the growth of roots in flowering and fruit plants.
- **forcing greenhouses** (also called cultivation greenhouses): these are greenhouses used for the cultivation of flowering and leafy plants, in order to promote their growth.
- **cultivation greenhouses**: these are the classic greenhouses used for the cultivation of garden plants.
- **drying greenhouses**: these are greenhouses which, as the definition itself states, are intended for the drying of agricultural products.

Greenhouses can also be classified according to their purpose. In that case we shall have them:

- **greenhouses for horticulture** (also called garden greenhouses): are greenhouses that are used for the cultivation of vegetables, which tend to be made of metal and plastic.

- **greenhouses for flowers** (also called greenhouses for floriculture): these are the greenhouses typically used for the cultivation of flowers.

- **garden greenhouses** (sometimes combined with ornamental greenhouses): these are greenhouses smaller than the usual ones, which allow even those who do not have large spaces, to grow their plants in greenhouses; their arrangement in the house, or in the garden of the house, means that the aesthetic care of this type of greenhouse is superior; also for this reason, especially indoor greenhouses, are also called ornamental greenhouses.

- **A particular type of greenhouse**, suitable for the cultivation of the winter garden, is the tunnel greenhouse. These are small greenhouses, which protect the vegetables during the coldest period of the year, without taking up much space.

From a constructive point of view, we recognize the existence of two types of greenhouses:

- **Double-pitched greenhouses**: These structures have asymmetrical and symmetrical pitches and are intended to produce flowers, succulents, vegetables and other crops. To encourage the passage of air, we suggest the installation of motorized openings. On this type of greenhouse, it is possible to install photovoltaic panels to support the environment.
- **Tunnel greenhouses** with semi-circular or elliptical vault: these structures are intended for the cultivation of tree crops and protected grapes. The materials generally used are polyethylene film. Also, in this case it is possible to install motorized or manual openings on the sides.

Temperature is also a peculiar feature of some greenhouses.

- **Cold greenhouses**: when they are not air-conditioned
- **Temperate greenhouses**: in this case the temperature is kept between 10 and 14°.
- **Hot greenhouses**: in this case the temperature can reach between 16° and 20°. If it exceeds 22° it will recreate a tropical climate.

Agrotextiles

Agro-textiles are means with an antifreeze or semi-freezing function. They are very large sheets of plastic, very light, which is placed over the crop without any support. This allows the plants to grow normally without any hindrance (at least up to certain limits).

The most common agro-textiles are permeable sheets made of polyester or pressed polypropylene fibre (called "non-woven fabric"), elastic and light. Their weight is about 17 g per square metre.

They are mainly suitable for autumn-winter or spring leaf vegetables: lettuce, chicory, radicchio, spinach.

Hydroponic greenhouses

Another type of greenhouse, which requires a separate chapter, are hydroponic greenhouses. These are greenhouses that exploit the principles of hydroponic cultivation. This type of cultivation does not use the soil, but only the water and nutrients necessary for plant development. This produces advantages, especially about the spread of certain plant diseases. In addition, by providing nutrients to the plant in a controlled manner, it is possible to modify the characteristics of its fruit. The hydroponic greenhouse, therefore, is a particular greenhouse that is based precisely on these principles. Many companies are trying to invest in this field, convinced that they can benefit from this type of cultivation.

Nicolas Campos

CHAPTER 2 - Garden Greenhouses

Cultivating is a passion that is often associated with the use of the greenhouse, if you want to have products always at hand or varieties that in cold weather would not survive in the open air.

There are many different types of greenhouse, knowing them will help us to understand which is best suited to our needs and our possibilities, not only economic, but also space. The choice also depends on what use we intend to make of them.

The most widespread and requested type of greenhouse is the economic and practical one. It is available on the market distributed in assembly kits, practical and quick to assemble, it takes about ten minutes. It costs little and is suitable for those who begin to try their hand at growing.

Usually the cheap greenhouse is suitable for those who have few vegetables and no aesthetic pretension, but simply seeks the essentiality of its function. This greenhouse can be disassembled and stored indoors after use, to be reassembled when it is needed again.

If you have never had to deal with a greenhouse, start with the cheap and practical greenhouse, it will help you to get familiar with this new way of growing vegetable garden and it will be a good training to then move on to other types of greenhouses, more demanding in maintenance and after all you can always reuse this greenhouse, since it is made to be assembled and reassembled in a few minutes.

Garden greenhouse cultivation for small spaces

Another type of greenhouse is the mini, perfect for those who do not have a large garden, but grow near the entrance of the house, in a small portion of land. The mini greenhouse is an easy, cheap and quite fast solution. You can find it in different materials: wood, metal or plastic. The choice of material also implies a difference in price.

The plastic mini greenhouse costs less than those made of wood or metal. The wooden ones are, however, the most popular, because they look like miniature closets that decorate the garden.

The mini greenhouse is a self-supporting structure leaning against it, divided into three zones, each with its own function. In the lower part the tools are stored together with fertilizer and soil (even if this area is often missing in the mini greenhouses, as in the one in the photo). In the central and upper part are placed the plants. Usually the central part is wide, for the taller plants, while in the upper part, aroma plants are placed.

Another type of greenhouse is the Victorian. The Victorian greenhouse is made of glass and metal, with doors and windows. It can be realized starting from the ground, as if it were a closed veranda, or using a lower part made of bricks, to reduce the cost of construction. The Victorian greenhouse is large, suitable for storing ornamental plants, but also for growing vegetables in winter, making the seedbed and storing tools and materials.

More than a greenhouse is considered an appendage of the house, where you can sit and chat with friends in cases where the space allows you to place a table with chairs inside it.

Finally, we have the pavilion greenhouse but one of the most fascinating.

The pavilion greenhouse has a hexagonal shape, built in wood and glass on a concrete base, with large windows on the sides and in some cases also on the roof, to allow more ventilation to the plants.

Greenhouses Features

Greenhouses are structures that respond to specific characteristics to ensure the right habitat for plants, flowers and vegetables.

Whatever their configuration, we start from the base. The floor must be of good quality for proper thermal insulation. The humidity must be kept at bay, so the floor must be solid and resistant.

Today most structures are made of steel, while the roof can be made of glass or plastic materials.

Glass is certainly much more resistant and lasts longer. In addition, it is often treated with metal oxides, so that unnecessary heat loss is avoided.

As far as plastic is concerned, polycarbonate (very common), PVC or reinforced polyester resins (typical of tunnel greenhouses) are used.

Air recirculation openings must be provided on the sides, especially during the summer season.

The door must be easy and comfortable, wide enough to allow the passage of tools and various materials.

Externally the presence of gutters or rainwater collection systems is recommended. In this way you can reduce the waste of water for irrigation.

Nicolas Campos

CHAPTER 3 - Building Types

As mentioned before, from a constructive point of view, greenhouses are essentially of two types:

- **double-pitched**, with symmetrical or asymmetrical pitches whose use is the production of vegetables, flowers, succulent plants, mushrooms and any other type of crops To improve ventilation inside the greenhouse it is possible to install, near the ridge and on the sides, motorized openings with movement by means of racks. This type of structure is suitable for mounting photovoltaic modules on the roof thanks to the adequate inclination of the pitches that allows the right incidence of sunlight on the photovoltaic panels.

- **a tunnel,** with semi-circular or elliptical vault whose use is the production of vegetables, flowers, mushrooms, tree crops and protected grapes. The covering and the perimeter covering are in polyethylene film, stretched on the structure by means of a roller winding system. In addition, depending on requirements, they can also be made with other types of plastic materials available on the market. In particular cases, to improve the ventilation of the environment it is possible to install motorized or manual openings near the eaves.

Climate control

Air conditioning a greenhouse means controlling not only the temperature but also the relative humidity, ambient light and air exchange.

The equipment of an air conditioning system in a greenhouse is fundamental to ensure the maintenance of the ideal temperature and humidity for plant growth.

In hot and temperate greenhouses, heating is the most important component. Not being enough the greenhouse effect to ensure the temperature, artificial heating is almost always indispensable.

It is generally obtained with unit heaters, i.e. hot air generators equipped with fans.

The most common type for heating air is the suspended type that blows hot air into a perforated plastic film pipe, which is also suspended.

For the heating of the growing substrate, instead, PVC pipes positioned inside the substrate or on the bottom of the pallet are used. In the cultivation on the ground, the pipes must be buried in one depth of 20-30 cm.

During the summer period the greenhouse effect creates problems of overheating, so it is necessary to cool the greenhouse. Using the combined effect of shading and natural or forced ventilation.

There are also systems that exploit the evaporation of water to produce cooling and that do not require shading.

These are called "cooling system" and "fog system".

- The "cooling system" consists of fans placed on a wall and a battery of humidifying honeycomb panels placed on the opposite wall. The fans, having to guarantee a frequent air change, have high flow rates and are chosen and positioned in such a way as to draw air at low speed from the humidifier panels. The quantity of water to be dosed on the panels is around 2 litres per m2 of panel.

- The "fog system" consists in the diffusion in the greenhouse of water sprayed at high pressure (35-40 bar) by nozzles mounted on pipes placed above the crop. The entire operating system of the modern greenhouses (shading screens, mechanized openings and closures, thermal regulation, etc.) can be managed entirely by computer based on the inputs transmitted by sensors and peripheral microprocessors.

Among the facilities on the market we can list:

- HEATING PLANTS: with the use of hot air or hot water generators (in case of above ground cultivation) powered by oil or solid fuels.
- SHADDING PLANTS: the use of shading fabrics allows to reduce the volume of air to be heated in order to reduce energy consumption. The sheets can be placed horizontally inside the greenhouse at eaves height, and their movement can be automated with the use of light and temperature sensors.

Ultimately, all systems can be fully automated by installing automatic control units connected to temperature, humidity and other necessary sensors.

Thermal accumulation in the ground

As is well known, temperatures in the soil are more constant than in the air and less affected by external climatic variations as the depth increases. These considerations have suggested the development of systems suitable for temperature stabilization in greenhouses based on forced air circulation inside corrugated pipes placed in the soil.

During the summer period the outside air entering the pipes at the fan is warmer than the ground.

As it passes through the underground pipes, it transfers its heat to the ground and comes out cooler and can cool the greenhouse. At the same time the ground heats up.

This technique has an interesting possibility of application in greenhouses in cold season.

The system involves the recirculation of the greenhouse air, with the accumulation of heat in the ground during the day and the return of heat during the night, with the result of keeping the temperature of the greenhouse higher during the night.

The system can be improved by providing accumulation systems consisting, for example, of tanks with a certain volume of water placed in the ground and crossed by air pipes.

Growing Techniques

Depending on the growing technique, a distinction should be made between greenhouses with soil cultivation and greenhouses with above-ground cultivation.

- **Soil cultivation**. Soil cultivation in a protected environment can be on the ground or on pallets. Pallets are normally made for ornamental plants and cultivation is done on natural or artificial substrates. They can be fixed or mobile. The fixed ones are generally made of prefabricated metal or concrete structures and are 1.6-2 m wide. The surface area used, given the need to leave the passageways free, hardly exceeds 75 % of that covered. The mobile pallets, due to the need for lightness and corrosion resistance, are generally made of aluminium. They have the same dimensions as fixed pallets but, since they can be

323

moved on rollers, the passage lane is not fixed but is created from time to time: this increases the usable surface area. Suspended pallets are also used; a solution that allows to have a surface used even more than 100% of the covered one. So-called "banquettes" are also used in ground cultivation. The ground of the greenhouse is divided into areas delimited by concrete slabs 20-30 cm high in order to create "beds" of cultivation width equal to or greater than one meter. Between one area and another, as with fixed pallets, there are lanes of passage. Unlike pallets, the growing substrate is not separated from the soil. Insulation can be achieved by placing a plastic film on the bottom and ensuring the drainage of irrigation water.

- **Cultivation above ground**. In greenhouses with above ground cultivation the most common form is based on the use of an inert and porous material (perlite, vermiculite, expanded clay, coconut fibre, pumice, etc.) as a substrate, on which a previously prepared nutrient solution is passed. Depending on the recovery of the nutritive solution, a distinction is made between closed and open cycle. Above ground crops represent a significant innovation introduced in the protected crops sector in recent years. Currently in Italy the technique is still not very widespread, involving about 7% of the entire surface area in protected crops, while in countries such as the Netherlands the percentage incidence exceeds 50%. Despite the advantage that this technique offers, especially in the management of mineral nutrition (also through software developed for this purpose that helps to calculate the amount of soluble salt to dissolve in water) and also in the greater control of diseases, above ground crops are difficult to spread, both for lack of cultivation of melons above ground and for the greater initial investment they require.

In the management of the nutrient solution, in addition to its chemical composition, the parameters to be kept under control are:

- the pH, which must be kept within an established range in order not to compromise the solubility of the nutrients and the exchange between the root system and the solution itself.

- the electrical conductivity, on which the control of the concentration of the nutritive solution depends (a low conductivity indicates an excessive dilution of the solution, while a high conductivity is equivalent to a high concentration and an excessive osmotic tension).

- the dispensing cycle and flow rates, from which the overall control of the mineral nutrition through the replacement of the solution is derived. Solution turnover requires careful management, especially for closed loop above ground crops. Management that, in order to be accurate, can only be computerized with dedicated software and based on calculation models related to the growth of the crop, the water consumption of the solution concentration, the salinity within the substrate.

On these aspects the research is very active, as well as the influence of the type of substrate and container of the same. A simplified hydroponic system developed at the beginning of the 1970s in England ("Nutrient Film Technique", NTF) involves the use of channels with an inclination of 1-1.5% protected at the top by an opaque plastic roof.

The pre-cultivated seedlings on inert materials (perlite, rock wool) are placed on the gutter in which the nutrient solution flows in a thin and continuous layer. In this way the roots are wetted by a veil of solution that is always in motion so there is no need to artificially aerate the solution.

Naturally, the nutrient solution is circulated by means of a pump with continuous control of pH and thermal conductivity.

Advantages of off-ground cultivation in peat or coconut fibre and perlite:

- increased production due to higher crop density (plants per linear metre).
- longer flowering time.
- fruit of constant size and homogeneous, high quality.
- optimisation of costs and working time, with a reduction in labour.

- protection of root systems from temperature changes thanks to the insulating power of expanded perlite.
- minimisation of risks of pests and pathogens.

Perlite is an effusive volcanic rock of variable colour between grey and pink, whose chemical composition is like that of rhyolites and dacite. Perlite can expand its volume up to 20 times its original volume when brought to high temperatures, close to its softening point. The expansion is linked to the presence of water that remains confined in the closed porosity of the rock as a result of the sudden cooling during the magma's escape.

When subjected to temperatures between 550 and 900° C, the rock expands due to the vaporization of the water: in this irreversible process bubbles are generated inside the granules of the bubbles that give the expanded rock the exceptional lightness that characterizes it, an extraordinary power of thermal insulation and the typical white colour.

Lighting

In Northern Europe, the reduced number of hours of daily lighting during the winter period severely limits the plant's growth possibilities. Artificial lighting is thus used. The electrical power normally installed is in the order of 50 W/m2.

Since a large part of the electrical energy is converted into heat, artificial lighting also contributes to heating.

Fluorescent lamps are mostly used, while incandescent lamps are not recommended because of their high consumption and the red-light band emitted unsuitable for plant growth.

Growing Techniques with Rfid Technology

In the Netherlands, the Walking Plant System (WPS), one of the leading suppliers of greenhouse management systems in the Netherlands, uses technology provided by companies specialising in the automatic identification of goods and people and in the development of software, by marking each individual flowerpot with a transponder (tag), the entire greenhouse cultivation process has been optimised. With this project, WPS has demonstrated how the use of Rfid (Radio Frequency Identification) technology can also be used in greenhouses. The system developed by integrating Rfid technology with image technology is fully automated throughout the entire life cycle of the plant, from sowing to sale to the end customer.

The management software ensures that each plant can receive a specific treatment, according to its needs. Thanks to Rfid technology also the sales management is automated with great reliability.

CHAPTER 4 - Design of a Greenhouse

When you worry about building a greenhouse, you must take into account that the materials to be used must be used for two different purposes: the first is to support the structure and therefore have a load-bearing function, the second is to convey heat, so you must choose a material that does not shield the construction too much.

Supporting Structure

Since their introduction, greenhouses are made of wood, a very economical material that can give some problems in the long run, breaking easily and changing with temperature changes.

To avoid major damage, if you have a higher budget, steel is certainly a good alternative: more resistant and less bulky than wood, this material is also useful to reduce heat loss.

However, the best choice for the supporting structure should be aluminium as it is extremely resistant. The only problem is its cost, certainly higher than the other alternatives.

Finally, if the greenhouse is small, plastic can also be a good option for the supporting structure.

Greenhouse Coverage

The strength of the greenhouse, as we explained in the previous lines, lies in its ability to store heat and this peculiarity depends on the type of material used for the roofing.

The choice of the right material is therefore essential and, bearing in mind that it must be transparent and able to filter light, there are various alternatives available:

- simple and polished glass
- raw glass, printed glass
- hammered glass

- striped glass

plastic with rigid, corrugated or smooth resin, polycarbonate or polyester sheets

As far as glass is concerned, there are many advantages to be listed because it is a transparent material, which resists humidity well and has a very high thermal insulation capacity; among the disadvantages there are certainly its heaviness and potential fragility.

Plastic, on the other hand, is decidedly lighter than glass and this will make it possible to choose less consistent (and cheaper) load-bearing structures; at the same time, plastic does not have the same level of transparency as glass, which could compromise the ultimate goal of the construction of the greenhouse itself.

Other useful tips and tricks

In order to avoid that all the work done to build the greenhouse is in vain, it is right to carry out thermal insulation work that will be able to minimize the internal heat loss.

This process involves the application of horizontal sheets of transparent polyethylene bubble on the outside of the structure; to fix them correctly, an air vacuum must be created between the vacuum and the roof.

In a greenhouse it is essential to organize the internal space in a rational and efficient way so that your work is as easy as possible.

The insertion of a worktable and metal pallets can help you achieve this, allowing you to position crops according to their need for sunshine.

Finally, don't forget to equip your greenhouse with water outlets, electrical sockets and artificial lights, one or more hot air generators, a thermometer and an automatic irrigation system.

Low-tech Greenhouses

For this type of greenhouses an investment of around 20-25 euros/m2 is required.

The structure is very simple, and the cover is made of plastic. The climate control is poor and often there is no heating system.

The species grown in these greenhouses are low-income vegetables and cut flowers. The cultivation technique is simple and does not differ much from that used in the open field. In the case of vegetables, these are often tunnel greenhouses.

Mid-Tech Greenhouses

For this type of greenhouses an investment of around 25-80 euro/m2 is required.

The structure is generally made of metal and both glass and plastic (often rigid panels) are used as covering material.

Climate control is more efficient than in the previous case and the internal environment is relatively independent from the external one; in the case of vegetables, however, they are often "cold greenhouses" (without heating or with emergency heating in case of frost).

Cultivation techniques are more advanced, and include hydroponic systems, with many partially or fully automated cultivation operations.

These greenhouses are used not only for growing vegetables out of season, but also for high value cut flowers (example rose) and potted ornamental plants.

Hi-Tech Greenhouses

For this type of greenhouses, the investment required is more than 80 euros/m2 and can reach or even exceed 160 euros/m2.

Generally, the supporting structure is made of galvanized iron and the covering material is glass. You have a sophisticated climate control, based on:

- heating of both the air and the root zone
- forced ventilation
- cooling and humidification systems (e.g. cooling system)
- light conditioning (artificial lighting and shading)
- carbon enrichment

The indoor climate can be completely independent of the outdoor climate. Cultivation systems are designed to maximise the efficiency of space use and minimise the use of labour.

These greenhouses are mainly used for the cultivation of ornamental plants and to produce propagation material in cold climate regions.

CHAPTER 5 - How to Build a DIY Greenhouse

The construction of a greenhouse is a demanding project; however, it can be carried out economically or perhaps by relying on professional builders.

Things you will need

- Mounting kit for greenhouses
- Tape measure
- Wooden beams
- Gravel
- Glass panels
- Glass fibre panels
- Double-walled plastic sheets
- PVC
- Iron rod
- Wire
- Stakes
- Wood treatment products
- Fans

- Thermometers
- Electric, wood or gas heating elements
- Breathers
- Cisterns
- Water
- Aiuole
- Tables for vases

Choice of Location

Choose an area with a southern exposure. The first requirement for a greenhouse is always to be exposed to plenty of sunshine.

All structures should be located north of the greenhouse.

A rather common form of construction for greenhouses is the one leaning against another building. In this case it is good to choose a south facing wall.

Places that are exposed to the sun in the morning rather than in the evening are preferable. The best option is always to have the sun all day long, but if this is not possible, exposure to the sun in the morning is more conducive to plant growth.

If there are trees or shrubs in the vicinity of the greenhouse, make sure they do not shine on the greenhouse until late afternoon.

Consider winter sunshine compared to summer sunshine. If the area facing east is open and sunny, you will get better sunshine from November to February.

The sun's rays in winter have less inclination, so trees, houses and other structures can cause more shade problems.

Do not choose a location near evergreen trees. Decaying trees lose their leaves and get less shade in winter, when the greenhouse needs more sun.

Choose a location where electricity is available. Many greenhouses require heating and ventilation to maintain the optimum temperature.

If you build a greenhouse against a house, you can get the energy you need through an extension of the house's electrical system.

Installing an electrical system in a separate building may require an electrician.

Choose an area with good drainage. You will need to drain the excess rainwater.

If the ground in the chosen area has hollows, you will probably need to fill them to improve drainage.

You can install rainwater tanks to collect rainwater from the roof of the greenhouse. Every form of saving water and energy supply helps to reduce the operating costs of the greenhouse.

Choice of Structure Type

Measure the available space. Whether you decide to build the greenhouse from scratch or with the help of an assembly kit, choose your dimensions carefully.

The larger the greenhouse, the higher the costs for construction and heating.

You can easily find greenhouses in assembly kits with dimensions of 2x3x1.8 m, or 3x6x1.8 m.

Choose a greenhouse in kit, if you have little experience in construction or if you do not have someone who can help you.

You can buy a small polycarbonate greenhouse in a mounting box at DIY stores or online at Amazon or eBay, starting from just over $60.

You can find larger and more robust models from $450 and up, depending on the size.

In addition to generic websites, you can look at the sites of chains that specialize in selling gardening materials.

Build a wall mounted greenhouse. If you have chosen an area adjacent to a building, you can build a simple structure against a wall.

If the wall is made of brick or concrete, the warmth of the building itself can help maintain a constant warmth.

This is a very simple structure that you can build yourself. You can build it with iron rods, tubulars, wooden beams; in general, it will need less support elements than a stand-alone construction.

Build a tunnel greenhouse. This is a type of greenhouse with a tunnel roof, which can be built with steel supports or PVC pipes.

The tunnel shape means less space in height and reduced storage capacity compared to rectangular models.

This type can be built with little expense; however, the cheapest materials are also generally the least robust.

Choose a rigid structure. For this type you will need to build foundations and a supporting structure. Unless you are an expert in building design, we recommend that you commission the project from a specialist or delegate the construction to someone else.

A rigid structure, made with support poles and beams, requires foundations and strong structural elements.

To build a large rigid greenhouse you will need the help of friends or professional bricklayers.

Choice of Covering Material

Uses polyethylene film for greenhouses, UV treated. The light transmission is like that of glass, but it is light and inexpensive.

The plastic film should be renewed after a few years.

It needs to be washed from time to time.

It does not retain heat as well as glass, but it is suitable for wall and tunnel greenhouses, and for small rigid greenhouses.

It uses rigid double-walled plastic material.

Polycarbonate lends itself to being slightly curved and allows energy savings of up to 30% thanks to the double wall.

It typically allows 80% of the light to pass through.

Choose glass fibre. If you want to build a rigid greenhouse, you can save money by using fibreglass instead of glass.

Choose transparent fiberglass.

You will need to restore the resin cover every 10-15 years.

You prefer high quality fiberglass. The light transmission is much lower in the case of low-quality glass.

Choose glass. This is the most beautiful material to see, if you intend to build a greenhouse to decorate your house or garden.

Glass is very fragile, and repairs are expensive.

You must necessarily build a greenhouse with a rigid structure with a foundation.

Tempered glass is preferable because it is more resistant than ordinary glass.

If you intend to pay the cost of installing a glasshouse, we recommend that you ask for offers from specialist builders to ensure that the foundation and structure are adequate to support the weight.

Building of the Structure

Tension wires on the ground to measure the position of the supports. Plant stakes in the ground.

Create iron rod reinforcements. If you are building a greenhouse against a wall or a tunnel greenhouse, you can create the structure with rod and PVC.

Plant the rods in the ground at a regular distance of 120 cm. Let it protrude about 120 cm.

Once the rods are in place, make arches from side to side with 6 m long PVC pipe sections. Spread the polyester sheet over the arch structure and fix it at the bottom to joists.

Pour gravel on the ground to form a homogeneous layer, after planting the supports in the ground. The use of well melted fine gravel promotes excellent drainage of the greenhouse.

If you need foundations, have masons do the work. They will assemble formwork and cast the greenhouse floor before the structure can be built.

Apply a protective treatment to all wooden parts before you put them in place.

Untreated wood rots within 3 years.

Choose carefully the type of treatment for the wooden parts. The use of certain treatment products does not allow the food produced to be considered "organic" due to the chemical compounds they contain.

Some wood treatment products are specifically designed to reduce leaching. Leaching is the process by which soluble elements of the soil are transported or migrate into the deeper layers as a result of water flow and percolation.

It is better to prefer metal support elements rather than wooden ones.

Seal the roof over the structure as well as possible. In the case of plastic film, you can fix it to the wood with bolts.

The more expensive the roofing material is, the more care you will have to take when sealing the roof connections to the foundations and the supporting structure.

Find out the best way to apply the cover you have chosen.

Check Temperature

Place fans in the corners of the greenhouse. Place them diagonally.

They should be on most of the time throughout the winter to ensure a homogeneous temperature throughout the greenhouse.

Install vents in the greenhouse ceiling. You can also place them near the top of the supports.

A certain degree of carbon dioxide ventilation is essential.

The vents should be adjustable. You will need to open them more in the summer months.

Consider installing an electric heating system. Depending on the climate, exposure to sunlight can contribute as little as 25% to heating. In these cases, some additional heating is indispensable.

You can also use a wood or kerosene stove, but this solution requires the installation of a chimney to ensure good air quality.

You should contact the municipal technical office to check which types of heating are allowed in your area.

Install an air conditioning system if yours is a glass-walled greenhouse. If you can afford to install a temperature control system you can grow practically anything.

Have a professional electrician install the system.

The system will require regular maintenance to ensure ventilation and heating during the winter.

Install thermometers or thermostats. Install more than one thermometer in case one fails.

Place them at different heights in the greenhouse.

You can install a thermometer that transmits the temperature measurement to a display inside the house, so you can comfortably keep an eye on the temperature of the greenhouse during the winter months.

Additional Design

Study the environmental conditions required by the plants you intend to grow. The more sensitive a species is to temperature and humidity conditions, the less likely it is to grow other species in the same area.

A cold greenhouse is a greenhouse designed to prevent plants from freezing. It is ideal as temporary protection.

A warm greenhouse is a greenhouse suitable for tropical plants.

Choose the desired temperature and keep it constant. It is not possible to create zones with different temperatures unless separating walls are installed.

Make sure you have adequate water availability. Ideally it should be water for irrigation or from tanks.

Build raised flowerbeds inside the greenhouse. You can also use tables with perforated shelves to help drain water.

If possible, build flowerbeds considering the height of the grower for ergonomic reasons.

CHAPTER 6 - Environmental Impact of Greenhouse Growing

Greenhouse cultivation causes a high environmental impact, which is expressed in:

- Defacement of the landscape and increase in the area of sealed soil.
- Waste disposal (roofing and other plastic materials, substrates, drainage solutions, etc.).
- Greenhouse gas emissions (heating systems).
- Intensive use of chemical products (fertilisers, pesticides, geopharmaceuticals, weed killers, herbicides, plant growth regulators) and water (often not of good quality). This causes problems of soil salinization, groundwater pollution, product contamination.
- Monoculture or in any case high crop specialization, thus causing a loss of biological "fertility" of soils due to accumulation of pathogenic organisms.

The area of Almeria, in Spain, is one of the most intensive in the world for the use of greenhouses. In Italy, Sicily is one of the regions with the highest number of greenhouses.

Data for Almeria are estimated annually:

- 1.1 t/ha of PE for roofing renewal (every 2-3 years)
- 112 kg/ha of plastic laces for plant tutoring
- 50 kg/ha of polypropylene colour traps for insects
- 500 kg/ha of plastic for irrigation systems and others, such as mulch residues, plastic coverings for greenhouse coverings, polystyrene containers used in nurseries, off-ground substrate residues (sacks), etc.

In the Netherlands, in heated greenhouses, 800 t/ha per year of CO_2 is released compared to 200 t/ha per year of CO_2 equivalent fixed by the crop: this balance represents the environmental and extra-seasonal cost.

The agroecosystem greenhouse is considered among those with the highest consumption of pesticides. For the phytosanitary protection of crops, an average of 10 chemical treatments/cultivation is carried out, with peaks that can exceed 20 interventions/cultivation for some floricultural species.

The annual quantity of pesticides used in Italy in intensive sericulture production is 47 kg/ha (active ingredient), in the Netherlands, on the other hand, it is about 31 kg/ha.

Not infrequently farmers use an excess of water and fertilizers compared to the actual needs of the plants.

For example, the supply of fertilizers in a tomato greenhouse in Sicily is about 6 t/ha per year, but only a certain percentage of nutrients is absorbed by the crop.

Excessive nutrient inputs compared to plant uptake result in problems of groundwater pollution (especially N) and accumulation of salts in the soil.

Increasing Sustainability.

Problems	Possible solutions
Landscape impact	Structural constraints and regulation of the expansion of covered areas in areas of landscape value by public administrations.
Plastic Disposal	Use of biodegradable plastic (mulching, small tunnels), long-life film (3-4 years, large tunnels), glass (greenhouses). Recycling of plastic materials.
Substrate disposal	Use of substrates that can be used for several cycles (ease of disinfection) and/or recyclable (e.g. organic substrates: compost, biomass for energy production).
Drainage solutions	Closed" cultivation systems (with irrigation water < 1 ds/m)
Gas emissions	Choose species and cultivars with low thermal requirements. Take measures to reduce heat loss (heat shields). Use basal heating.

	Use alternative energy sources (e.g. organic residues) or renewable energy sources (solar, wind, biomass, etc.). Use the gases produced by heating for carbon enrichment of the greenhouse.
Soil salinization	Correct management of irrigation and fertilization. Rainwater harvesting.
Massive use of pesticides	Integrated and biological fight. Use of resistant cultivars. Steam disinfection;
Organic soil weariness	Adoption of long rotations. Off-ground cultivation systems. Use of resistant cultivars. Grafting on resistant rootstocks

Nicolas Campos

CHAPTER 7 - Programming of Planting for Growing throughout the Year

What to Grow in the Cold Greenhouse?

In a cold greenhouse we can grow practically all vegetable garden crops, usually depending on the size you decide what to plant indoors and what to leave outdoors.

Among the most efficient plants to keep in the tunnel are salads, carrots, radish, beets and spinach. These plants take up little space and are well suited to spring and winter, offering good resistance to cold. Summer fruit vegetables such as solanaceae and cucurbitaceae are bulkier and require a greenhouse of good size.

Growing vegetables in the greenhouse is not very different from growing them in the open-air garden, but there are some significant differences. Firstly, the roofing not only protects against the cold but also limits the air circulation and protects against rain. This means that the grower must provide proper irrigation and airing the indoor space properly.

Very important is the choice of the position where to put our greenhouse: it must be sunny and easy to access for us.

Inside the greenhouse we can apply the same general principles valid for the outdoor garden: subdivision of the flowerbeds and walkways, arrangement of the drip system, mulching, sowing some flowers that attract pollinators and eco-friendly methods of fertilization and defence against adversity.

If the greenhouse is big enough, we can afford to keep at least the first meter of length as a space of movement, to support the tools, seeds and seedlings that we are going to use, to keep a service table, a chair, the bin full of water for irrigation, etc..

Period in which to use it

The cold greenhouse can be used practically all year round. Without any doubt, it is better to exploit it in full during the months of January-March in the south,

February-April in the north, and also for the whole autumn, because these are precisely the periods in which having a greenhouse can make a great difference.

In this way, the production of spinach, various types of lettuces, chard, rocket and other vegetables can be prolonged.

When you go towards winter the greenhouse may still contain vegetables, but in periods when temperatures fall below zero it is good to cover them with non-woven cloth.

During the summer, on the other hand, very high temperatures can be generated inside the greenhouse and cultivation is only possible if the structure can be opened well on the sides. It may also be advisable to cover the roof of the greenhouse with shading nets in case of strong sunlight.

Inside the greenhouse (as mentioned above) we will have to provide irrigation, and for this purpose it certainly makes sense to set up a drip system, to encourage a gradual distribution of water without excesses.

However, it may be worthwhile to make sure to collect rainwater by fixing gutters along the long sides of the greenhouse, at the top, which will introduce the water that falls on the greenhouse in drums below. If the greenhouse is small, we can also irrigate manually by filling the watering can with water from these bins. It is useful to keep other bins full inside the greenhouse, to let the water cool down for some time before using it.

Sloping roof greenhouses usually have windows at the sides and/or on the roof, in addition to the doors, while tunnels generally offer the possibility of opening the sides.

When choosing a prototype greenhouse, it is advisable to take this into account, because during the hot hours of the day it is important to open the greenhouses to circulate air and disperse moisture, which favours the onset of fungal diseases.

In the long run, the cover of the greenhouse can become dirty and opaque, limiting the entry of light, and if there are trees nearby, it is possible that leaves may accumulate on the upper part. As a result, periodic cleaning is always necessary to ensure good lighting efficiency indoors.

With a small structure of about 2 x 3 m or 2 x 4 m we can already obtain some discreet family productions, but if possible it is better to choose a larger one, for example a tunnel measuring 3 x 10 m, which can allow us to diversify the crops and give us satisfaction.

However, in general it makes sense to relate the size of a greenhouse to the total area of the garden, considering the uncovered crops and the space they require.

A large greenhouse also allows us to allocate part of the surface area to the seedbed activity to produce seedlings and cuttings of perennial species, and this is also an interesting aspect.

For good ventilation, the greenhouse should have two doors, or at least openable roofs and openings on the sides. Depending on the structure and the size, the methods for changing air will vary. In tunnels you usually lift the tarpaulin on the side.

Let's summarize what to grow in the greenhouse in winter

Here is a list of what you can grow in the unheated greenhouse in the middle of winter:

- salads,
- radishes,
- valerianella,
- spinach,
- onions,
- garlic,
- turnips,
- cabbages,
- chicory,
- radicchio,
- parsley,
- celery,
- carrots,

- fennel,
- Brussels sprouts,
- wild strawberries,
- tomatoes

Those who live in northern Italy should not dare to grow tomatoes under a greenhouse if they do not have a heated greenhouse. This is because the tomato could also lead to the production of fruits but, because of the cold, it would give you tomatoes that are not very juicy and have inadequate organoleptic properties.

Some recommended greenhouse models

- **Greenhouse Kenley** 3×2. Small and versatile tunnel greenhouse, with steel structure and roll-up tarpaulin.
- **Outsunny** greenhouse 4.5×2. Other tunnel model, slightly larger than Kenley, with iron tubular structure and ventilation windows.
- **Tunnel lock** 6×3. Larger size greenhouse, up to 2 meters high, with good value for money. Double door and good opening system with roll-up tarpaulin on the sides.

- **TecTake** greenhouse of 11 square meters, with aluminium structure and polycarbonate walls. A greenhouse beautiful to see, therefore suitable for vegetable garden contexts in the garden, equipped with door and windows on the sloping roof. The materials make it quite expensive.
- **Mini greenhouse Valmas**. Ingenious roofing system, very easy to place and well resistant. Suitable for quick interventions to protect the winter garden from unforeseen cold or spring crops in case of late frost.

CHAPTER 8 - Seedbed Guide

Most of the vegetables we know are not sown directly in the garden but are grown starting with transplanting.

The seedlings can be bought from nurseries or trusted shops, but learning how to get them on your own is a great step forward: it allows you to save money and to grow for each species just the varieties we are interested in, since the purchase of seed sachets can be organized in time and with a good choice compared to that of the ready seedlings.

By seedbed or nursery, we mean a transparent structure, usually covered with plastic sheets, glass or Plexiglas and whose function is to offer a warm microclimate to the plants growing inside.

Why sow in Seedbeds?

The advantages that the seedbed technique offers compared to direct sowing in the garden are various and interesting.

Select seedlings. First, we can sow more seedlings than those that are really needed in the garden, so when they are ready, we will have the possibility to choose the best and the most uniformly developed ones.

Optimize the space in the garden. With seedlings spending the first phase of their life in the seedbed, they keep the garden beds occupied for a shorter time, and these can be used for other crops beforehand. Think of all those species that are only transplanted at the end of April or May, for example pumpkins: if we sowed them directly in the garden we would have to do so at the beginning of April, and the space would then already be occupied a month earlier, perhaps not allowing spinach or salads to be grown on that same space previously.

Anticipate sowing. The seedbed is a sheltered place, where it is possible to sow a few weeks earlier than direct sowing, as the internal temperature is higher.

Less weeding work. You must consider that the transplanted seedlings have an advantage over the weeds, even if soon we will still have to intervene by hoeing or mulching.

Economic savings. Finally, there is the saving on the purchase of the seedlings, which will soon pay back the small initial investment to set up the structure.

Which vegetables are suitable for the seedbed?

Even if most horticultural crops can be grown in seedbeds, it is important to know that some species do not tolerate transplanting, so it is good to know which crops are suitable for sowing in trays.

All cucurbits lend themselves very well to transplanting pumpkin, courgette, melon, watermelon and cucumber. The technique is also valid for pepper, chilli, aubergine, tomato, head lettuce, chard, celery, cabbage and other vegetables.

Usually, those species that are to be placed at well-defined distances in the garden are transplanted, while it would be less convenient for the species that are placed in a continuous row, such as rocket and parsley, or peas and beans, because in this way too many seedlings would be needed and therefore it would be better to sow directly in rows. Some farms, however, transplant rocket, spinach and parsley, because with the direct sowing in rows the rapid birth of weeds would then make it problematic to keep the row clean and therefore prefer to transplant the tufts of 3-4 seedlings on black perforated sheets.

For carrots, turnips and radishes transplanting is not recommended because the rooting of the seedlings is difficult, being a root species, it is better to sow directly in the garden, in order to obtain a more regular vegetable of good size.

If we have little space for the seedbed, we must make a choice between seedlings to sow and those to buy. In this case it is preferable to buy leek and onion seedlings because they are placed in the garden at short distances and you need a lot of them: we would risk investing all our small seedbed space only with these. In addition, leek and onion seeds can be stored for a maximum of 2 years, so if there are any open sachets left over, they may expire before they are fully used.

Buy or build the structure

If you practise carpentry and manual work amuses us, you can build a wooden or alternatively metal support structure yourself, which you can then cover with transparent material. The do-it-yourself seedbed is not difficult to do, the important thing is to provide convenient openings to perform all the necessary operations afterwards.

If we opt instead for the purchase of the seedbed greenhouse, the expense to buy it will still be amortized in a relatively short time, given the savings on the purchase of seedlings, you can choose from many different solutions that you find on the market, you must select the most suitable according to the size and characteristics.

Seedbed characteristics

As we have already seen the seedbed is a wooden or metal structure with walls and transparent cover (so glass, plastic sheet or plexiglass panels), we see that other characteristics must have as dimensions and positioning.

Seedbed position

In order to position our small greenhouse, you must prefer a sunny position but also sheltered from the winds. The seedbed can be placed directly in the vegetable garden but in this way, it takes away useful space for cultivation, so it is good to consider other sunny corners outside this area. Given the frequent care that seedlings require, it is essential that the seedbed is close to the place where you live or work, or alternatively have collaborations for daily care. In fact, the production of seedlings could be an important shared activity between several garden growers.

There are no limits to the size of a seedbed greenhouse, we must rely on the possibilities of space we have. Ideally the space to put the seedlings should be related to the surface of the garden. Usually a few square meters are enough, in which to exploit also the verticality with various shelves, if it is done without sacrificing light.

If the seedbed has the conformation of a real greenhouse for vegetable garden, however small, it is useful to put inside it one or more work tables that we need to do the sowing and then to keep all the containers lined up there. Obviously, if it is a small-scale seedbed, the work will be done outside, and no furniture is needed except the spaces where to put the sowing trays.

Heating

Having a heated seedbed can be very useful to advance sowing and earn a few weeks. A sheltered room with walls that let in light already tends to create a higher temperature than the room, but sometimes heating is useful. In order not to dissipate energy unnecessarily, it is better to heat a small seedbed to germinate the seeds.

For this purpose, you can use cheap mats, we have gone into the article on how to heat the seedbed.

What does it take to sow?

Once the structure has been built, we'll get to work, so let's see what we need for sowing: from the pots to the soil, all the way to the seeds.

Plant Containers

For sowing we can start to keep all the black trays that were sold to us with the previous seedlings, but it may be necessary to buy others. The black colour of these trays has the function of rapidly heating the soil inside them and speeding up the birth of the seedlings. In theory you can sow in any small container of small size, piercing the bottom to avoid dangerous stagnation of excess water, in small scale you can use, for example, jars of recycled yoghurt, in practice, however, to optimize space is better to choose the classic trays for seedlings, which have a low cost and allow you to better organize the seedbed.

An environmentally sustainable alternative to classic plastic or polystyrene trays is the soil blocker system, which also has great advantages on the cultivation side.

Which soil to use?

For substrates it is good not to choose the classic universal potting soil, because it contains some coarse material, not functional to put small seeds in a jar. The professional potting soil for sowing is finer and therefore better, but over time we can also learn to use less potting soil by mixing it with soil and compost, both previously sieved.

A good recipe for producing your own seeding soil is to mix vegetable garden soil, silica sand and brown peat (you can make a third for each component). The use of earthworm humus in the substrate is also positive, as well as nourishing helps the rooting.

There are also some ready-made peat disks (like the ones you can find here), this is a much cheaper solution, although more convenient. Those who cultivate on the balcony can choose it for not having around bags of soil that dirty.

To grow an organic vegetable garden, you should choose seeds that come from organic farming, or at least have not been tanned with fungicides. Ideally it is also useful to learn how to preserve and reproduce the seeds of some vegetables, so this operation is simple, such as tomatoes and peppers.

How to plant the seedlings?

There are species with large seeds, such as zucchini and cucumbers, for which sowing is very simple. In each hole of the black trays, completely filled with soil, we can put a single seed from which a seedling will be born.

For species with small seeds, such as lettuces, cabbage, chicory or peppers, it is better to spread on the wet soil in a small bowl many seeds to be covered with a thin layer of soil passed through a sieve. So many seedlings will be born, and we will soon put them through a marking out, the technique that consists of gently extracting the seedlings and replant them in new containers with soil, each in its own compartment of tray. This operation must be done when the seedlings are very small and have a long but still little branched root. For the picking we help ourselves with a stick to gently push the root of the seedling into the potting soil. The seedlings usually take root without problems and grow independently of each other, each with its own soil bread. There are also those who let them all grow together and separate them only at the time of transplanting, but usually the seedlings grown together look a bit spunky, because they have taken light away from each other.

Remember to put labels to indicate which vegetable you have sown in each jar; you can also make very pretty ones.

When to sow the different species

Among the first seedlings of the season that we are going to sow in the seedbed are head lettuces and Cataluña chicory, which are born at only 4 or 5 °C. Soon we can continue with chard, cabbage, borage and tomatoes, and when temperatures are mild, we sow cucurbits, pepper, basil and aubergine.

For autumn vegetables (all cabbage and various endives and chicory) we sow from June to July, while fennel is sown only in July and transplanted in August, because anticipating the sowing of fennel before June 21 exposes it to the risk of pre-flowering. To avoid this, in fact, the days must have started to shorten, and July is the most suitable period.

For these summer sowings, however, the seedbed must always remain open on the sides, acting at that point as a roof that protects the plants from thunderstorms and summer hailstorms.

For certain species sowing can be staggered and is a very recommended choice because it allows to obtain harvests distributed over time. Lettuce, chard, courgette, cucumber, cucumber, cabbage and leek are very suitable for sowing.

After sowing

Let's see what care needs to be taken in the seedbed after planting the seed, to encourage sprouting and then let the seedlings develop correctly.

Irrigations in the seedbed

The seedlings should be watered with the watering can equipped with a shower, for a gentle jet, you can also use a nebulizer. Watering does not have to be daily because it depends on the weather conditions. In spring there are very humid and still cold periods during which the soil of the plants does not dry every day, as well as very hot and sunny days during which it may be necessary to water twice a day. The only certain rules are to check and observe well the state of the soil and the seedlings and irrigate when necessary, preferring the cool hours of the day to do so.

Precautions

There are basically two precautions to be taken for the care of seedlings in seedbeds:

Water with water at room temperature, keeping a full container inside the seedbed or mixing the tap water so that it is warm. Cold water can in fact induce stress to the seedlings.

Air the seedbed during hot days, opening all the openings to circulate air and avoid condensation. In the evening, however, it is always good to close the structure.

Possible diseases and pests of the seedlings

The seedlings in the seedbed can be eaten by snails, so if there is any doubt that they can enter, it is better to distribute around the sowing containers some iron orthophosphate, a slug killer allowed in organic farming.

Nicolas Campos

We can also note the onset of fungal diseases, favoured by the humid microclimate that is established in these environments, and among these we remember the pythium which, together with others, causes the death of the seedbeds. It is necessary to manage this inconvenience by treating with a product based on the antagonist fungus Thricoderma. If we manage to save the seedlings from the disease and transplant them, it will then be appropriate to disinfect the containers in which they have been immersed for a few hours in water and vinegar.

When the seedlings are to be transplanted

To understand when the seedlings are ready you need to make some observations and know the stage of those that are sold. The head lettuces and beets in general have formed at least 4 leaves, the tomatoes are about 15 cm tall, but the final proof is that extracting the soil block from the alveolus the roots hold it all and this does not crumble. If we see that the roots are all too wrapped and developed around the soil block this is a sign that we have waited longer and to confirm this we will notice that the seedling starts to yellow, because that soil is no longer sufficient. After transplanting it generally recovers, but it is always good not to get to this point.

From sowing to transplanting there is not always a defined time, because the germination and development of the seedlings are related to the temperature of the environment. Seedlings sown in February may arrive after a month and a half to transplant, while those sown in late spring are ready much earlier.

Once they are ready, the seedlings do not need to be transplanted immediately, but it is advisable to take them out of the greenhouse, keeping them still in the containers to acclimatize for a day or two, and only after transplanting them in the space we have chosen for them in the garden.

CHAPTER 9 - Sowing, Germination and Transplantation

Seeding Techniques

In order to increase and improve the uniformity of sowing and germination for vegetable species characterized by small and irregular seeds (e.g. carrot, celery, endive, onion, etc.), techniques have been developed:

- Pelleting
- Calibration
- Pre-germination

Pelleting

Sugar coating of the seed consists in externally surrounding the seeds with different materials based on clay and/or vermiculite. Vermiculite facilitates germination of the seeds, which can occur even in less than optimal conditions of humidity. Other substances, such as pesticides, fertilisers and hormones, can also be mixed with the sugar-coating material.

Recently, another method of sugar coating, called split pills, has been developed. Through this system, the sugared material in contact with soil moisture detaches from the seed. However, however, it is necessary that the moisture is optimal to prevent the sugared material from sticking to the seed and causing burns to the seedlings.

The technique of sugared almonds has become particularly popular in precision seeding for small seed species (e.g. lettuce, chicory and endive).

Calibration

Calibration is a technique that consists of selecting the various types of seeds according to their size.

Among the advantages that this practice has, are:

- Simultaneity in germination and emergence of seedlings
- Tolerance to suboptimal temperatures
- Uniformity of growth of seedlings

- Possibility of using precision seed drills more efficiently
- Contemporary collection of the production.

The calibration technique has been developed not only for small seed species, but especially for many F1 hybrid cultivars.

For F1 hybrids, sizing and counting improves the use of the product, because they are higher cost seeds that are marketed according to their number and not according to their weight.

Pre-germination

Pre-germination is a technique that consists in reducing the germination and emergency period of the seedlings, through the simple and traditional system of seed moistening.

This system is widespread for vegetable species belonging to the Cucurbitaceae family (e.g. zucchini, pumpkin, watermelon and melon).

The seeds are immersed in warm water for about 24 to 48 hours and then transferred to a warm, dark environment in the presence of peat until the radicle is released. Once pre-germinated, the seeds are placed in jars and then planted in the greenhouse. This technique is particularly applied to early-cycle spring species in order to anticipate their germination.

Pre-germination has then been successfully extended also for direct sowing in open field in order to ensure regular and simultaneous germination even under unfavourable conditions.

In this case, germination is first carried out under favourable conditions, after which sowing is carried out using well equipped machines, which deposit the pre-germinated seed on a substrate that ensures the emergence of seedlings.

The methods that can be used are:

1) Pre-germination in gelatinous substrates (fluid drilling)

This method consists of distributing the pre-germinated seed in a gel-like substrate through an injection machine. The method is suitable for humid climates and clayey soils, as the gel rapidly disintegrates.

2) Pre-germination in solid substrates (plug mix)

This method, on the other hand, consists in having the seed pregerminated on a substrate based on peat and/or vermiculite to be followed by their localized distribution with specific machines.

In this sense, cubes of peat-based substrate are produced, containing 2 - 3 germinated seeds which are then spaced according to the required crop density so that the germination process can continue for a certain period even under unfavourable environmental conditions.

This method has been developed in Italy particularly for precision sowing of industrial tomatoes in environments that are not favourable to germination and for delayed sowing.

Germination

Seed germination is the sum of all the morphological, physiological and biochemical phases that seeds undergo in order to generate a new plant.

For the germination process to take place, four conditions must be met:

- The embryo of the seed is vital
- There must be no physiological, physical or chemical (dormancy) obstacles to the germination process.
- The environmental conditions (temperature and humidity) are favourable.

Germination must take place rapidly, both to limit the phase of permanence in the seedbed and to reduce the parasite attacks that can be caused by the seed and the new seedling.

The germination of seeds takes place in three very distinct phases which are:

Phase 1: Awakening of the seed (activation).

Phase 2: Digestion and distribution of seed substances.

Phase 3: Development of the seedling.

Phase 1: Awakening of the seed can in turn be divided into three other sub-phases which are:

- Seed imbibition
- Synthesis of enzymes and hormones
- Rootle leak.

The seed imbibition phase is the one that occurs immediately after the seed has passed the dormancy phase.

In this phase, the seed becomes permeable to oxygen and water and hydrates in turn. The hydration, therefore, favours the activation of the germination process.

The synthesis of enzymes and hormones, provides an activation of the metabolic processes of the seed, characterized by:

An increase in enzymatic activity (in particular, enzymes that degrade sugars).

An increase in the breathing process

An increase in the degradation processes of the seed reserve substances (starch, lipids and proteins)

Inflow of soluble molecules to the embryonic tissues of the growing seed.

Also, from the point of view of the hormonal picture, there is a decrease in germination inhibitory hormones (ABA = abscisic acid) and a corresponding increase in germination promoting hormones (auxins, gibberellins and cytokinins).

The activation of the seed ends with the rootlet leaking from the seed, preceded by an intense growth phase of the embryo, during which the structure leaks from its envelope.

During Phase 2 of digestion and distribution of the seed substances, the reserve substances (starch, lipids, proteins, etc.), degraded to soluble and simpler substances (glucose, fatty acids and amino acids), are then transferred into the growth tissues.

Finally, once we reach Phase 3 where the structure of the seedling is now evident, it is possible to observe an axis where the cotyledons (i.e. the primordial leaves) are inserted.

On this axis it is possible to distinguish the radicle (the part that will develop downwards that will originate the roots) and the plumula (the part that will develop upwards that will originate the stem and leaves).

The germination of the seed in turn depends on intrinsic and extrinsic factors.

The intrinsic factors are related to the genetic characteristics of the species, such as:

- Species
- Variety
- Presence of hormones.

The extrinsic factors are instead related to environmental characteristics, such as:

- Water
- Temperature

- Oxygen
- Light
- Health status.

Germinability and viability of seeds

Knowledge of the process and the factors that regulate seed germination, is fundamental both for direct sowing in the open field and in the setting up of seedbeds in greenhouses, in order to understand what the optimal conditions are in order to obtain a prompt germination of the seeds and a uniform growth of the seedlings.

For this reason, the germination of a seed is influenced by its vitality and germinability.

The vitality of a seed is the characteristic of maintaining the physiological functions unchanged over time.

This property depends on the:

- Intrinsic characteristics (species and varieties)
- Extrinsic characteristics (e.g. growing environment, temperature and humidity of the species).

Depending on the vitality of the seeds, herbaceous species can be classified:

1. Short-lived (about 3 years e.g. chicory and lettuce)
2. Intermediate life (about 4 years e.g. barley, bean, rye, wheat and spelt)
3. Long life (about 5 years and more e.g. onion, chard, chickpea, watermelon, melon, pumpkin and zucchini, carrot, lettuce, tomato, eggplant and corn).

The germinability of a seed is the percentage probability that a viable seed will give rise to a new plant.

For this reason, from a commercial point of view, it is necessary that the seeds have minimum germinability values, which in turn vary according to specific characteristics.

Based on the percentage values of germinability, the species are divided into:

1. low germinability 65% (e.g. basil, carrot, endive, radicchio, parsley, pepper and aubergine)

2. Medium - low germinability 70% (e.g. asparagus, chard, cauliflower, broccoli, fennel, radish and celery)

3. Medium germinability 75% (e.g. watermelon, cabbage, Savoy cabbage, Brussels sprouts, melon, courgette, thistle, lettuce, common bean, tomato and spinach)

4. Highly germinal 80% (e.g. turnip, cucumber, pumpkin, Spanish bean, pea and broad bean).

The temperature is certainly the most important factor regulating seed germination, together with the optimal humidity conditions of the growing medium.

Depending on the optimal germination temperatures, horticultural species are divided into:

- At high temperature requirements 30 - 35 °C (pumpkin, courgette, watermelon, melon, etc.).

- At medium temperature requirements 20 - 30 °C (tomato, pepper, aubergine, etc.).
- At low temperature requirements 20 - 25 °C (lettuce, celery, spinach and asparagus).

The period required for seed germination is also linked to the thermal conditions of the growing medium.

About the moisture content of the substrate as a factor regulating the germinability of a seed, the species are divided into:

1. At low humidity level with conditions close to the withering point P.A. (e.g. pumpkin, melon, watermelon, pepper and radish)
2. At medium humidity level (e.g. cucumber, bean, pea, carrot, onion, spinach and tomato)
3. High humidity with conditions close to C.C. field capacity. (e.g. lettuce, chard and celery).

Horticultural species, unlike tree species, do not show phenomena of seed dormancy, at least the commercial ones regularly preserved and dried. In this case the lack of germination is due to the presence of old or badly preserved seeds.

An exception to this last characteristic are the species belonging to the Umbellifer or Apiaceae family (carrot, celery, fennel and parsley), where the reduced germinability of the seeds is due to the presence of embryos that are not very mature or absent despite the presence of reserve substances.

Seed quality

The quality of the seed is an important and fundamental requirement to be considered both in the case of direct sowing in the open field and to produce seedlings in nurseries for transplanting.

The quality of the seed is for this in turn dependent on:

1. Germinability of the seed
2. Seed purity
3. Calibration uniformity
4. Seed health
5. Genetic heritage of the variety.

Seed health can be easily verified in the laboratory with incubation tests in selective substrates that can detect the presence of phytopathogenic bacteria. In order to identify viruses, a visual and accurate control of freshly germinated seedlings is required.

The genetic characteristics of the variety can only be evaluated in the field and when the plants and seeds are harvested. This requires the use of certified seed with high germination guarantees and genetic resistance to diseases corresponding to those declared.

Plant Transplanting

Transplanting is the technique of planting seeds, which involves a phase of breeding the seedlings in greenhouses, before being transferred in open field.

Among the advantages of the technique we remember:

1.   Advance of the production cycle
2.   Earlier production (e.g. spring production) both in the open field and in greenhouses
3.   Shorter growing cycle than a plant sown directly
4.   Land use for several crops in the same year
5.   Elimination of failures
6.   Less competition with weeds
7.   Greater uniformity of growth of seedlings

8.   Better spacing of seedlings

9.   Possibility of using transplanting machines (working capacity of 1 ha of about 6 - 12 hours)

One of the disadvantages will be:

- Higher costs for setting up the nursery and seedbeds.
- Rooting problems of seedlings
- Shallower root system
- Plants most subject to water stress
- Plants most prone to transplant stress

The very expensive transplanting technique, mainly used for F1 hybrid vegetables or plants available in small quantities, involves structuring a horticultural nursery with the production of plants precisely and without losses.

A modern horticultural nursery is organised as follows:

1. Receipt of order
2. Substrate control.

a. Purchase.

b. Chemical/physical analysis.

c. Phytotoxicity test.

d. Preparation.

3. Seed control.

   a. Purchase.

   b. Germinability tests.

   c. treatments before germination.

4. Sowing programming.

5. Sowing in containers.

6. Germination in humid chambers or climatic cells.

   a. Staking.

   b. Repotting.

7. Transfer of seedlings to growth greenhouses.

   a. Acclimatisation.

   b. Irrigation.

   c. Fertilisation.

   d. Pesticide treatments.

e. Use of phyto regulators.

f. Hardening.

8. Packing and shipping.

9. Recovery and sterilization of containers.

Production of plants intended for transplanting

The production of the seedlings in a horticultural nursery, to be destined to the following transplanting, can be done by resorting to:

- Bare-root seedlings
- Floor plans with earthen bread.

In a horticultural nursery, the production of seedlings with earthen bread can be carried out using the following systems, such as:

1. Sowing in paper jars

2. Sowing in honeycombed containers

3. Sowing in peat jars

Sowing in paper jars involves the use of hexagonal section jars (paper pots), glued together and placed on recoverable aluminium trays.

The paperpots:

1. They are produced in different sizes (from 3 to 10 cm)
2. They are used according to the needs of the crops
3. Large-scale processing lines suitable for automatic filling and/or sowing are used
4. In the most efficient solutions, the glue that holds the jars together can be peeled off with water in order to facilitate the spacing and planting of the seedlings.

Sowing in honeycombed containers consists in the use of polystyrene or polypropylene containers, from which the seedlings can be extracted with the substrate together with the roots.

This system provides:

1. Production of automated lines for filling and sowing
2. More advanced solutions with automatic sowing of about 400 boxes per hour
3. Filling of about 20 to 150 cavities using 2 people

Finally, sowing in peat jars involves the use of peat to pack containers in 80-litre bales that are humidified at the time of use.

This system allows:

1. Elimination of the problem of jars
2. The seedlings are separated from the cube at the time of planting.
3. Use of dicing machines able to produce cubes from 3 to 7 cm with an hourly capacity of 2000 - 12000 cubes.
4. Precision Sowing
5. Use both naked and candied seeds.

The main substrates used for sowing in nurseries are mixtures based on:

1. Blond peat

2. Brown peat
3. Perlite
4. Vermiculite.

The substrates before they are used, they must be:

1. Chemically controlled
2. Physiologically controlled (with plant growth tests)
3. Checked from a phytosanitary point of view for toxic residues of salts and/or pesticides and pests.

The stages following sowing in containers shall include

1. Transfer of the containers to humid chambers for a few days, with high humidity and temperature between 15 and 25 °C.
2. Constant wetting of containers and seedlings by automatic irrigation to shorten germination times and uniformity of births

3. Once the emergence of the seedlings has occurred, staking is carried out to standardise the subsequent growth

4. Transfer of seedlings into larger containers

5. Hardening stage. Hardening is the technique that aims to increase the resistance of young seedlings to physical, water, chemical, transport and transplanting stresses before they are marketed. The hardening technique is carried out by trying to stimulate cross resistance, according to which a seedling, when subjected to slight stress, becomes resistant to stress of a different nature. Hardening makes it possible to increase the dry matter content in the plant and consequently reduce its moisture content in order to increase resistance to cold, especially for early spring sowing vegetable varieties.

The hardening of seedlings can be achieved by using various systems such as:

1. Use of reduced water regimes (during the last 10 days of nursery stay)

2. Use of differentiated temperatures (with modification of the morphological and physiological characteristics of the seedling)

3. Controlling plant nutrition through balanced regimes

4. Use of chemical substances (CCC cycocel or PP-333 pacobutrazole), capable of modifying the growth of the seedlings.

CHAPTER 10 - How to Regulate Atmospheric Humidity and Temperature

The two main elements to be managed in an unheated greenhouse and tunnel are atmospheric humidity and temperature, elements that affect crops. As a general rule, the optimum atmospheric humidity to be recorded during the winter in these protections must be 60-70 %, while the minimum temperature must be around 2-3 °C, values which occur using a hygrometer and a thermometer recording the maximum and minimum temperatures respectively.

Atmospheric Humidity

The atmospheric humidity, which is spontaneously created in a greenhouse and in an unheated tunnel, must always be kept under control, especially during the coldest periods, when the formation of water drops on the inner wall of the roofing sheets of the structures is not uncommon, water falling on the crops causes widespread and dangerous rotting.

If high, that is close to 80-90%, the atmospheric humidity settles also on the vegetables keeping them wet for long time, causing rottenness of fungal origin. For this reason, it is necessary to favour the exchange of air in the protections to eliminate the excess atmospheric humidity by intervening on the openings.

In autumn, spring and summer it is not difficult to regulate the atmospheric humidity inside the protections.

The operation is more complicated during the winter, when it is also necessary to maintain the minimum growth temperature of the vegetables (which generally ranges from 3 to 5°C).

During the coldest periods, it is necessary to avoid airing the protections in the early morning hours, as the extremely rigid external temperature would lower the internal one, taking advantage, on the contrary, of the "less cold" temperatures of the central hours of the day, providing for the closing of the openings before sunset, in such a way that the last sun of the day favours the increase of the internal temperature, useful to counteract the night thermal decrease.

Opening the protections during the winter for a few hours a day (i.e. in the order of 2-3) is enough to keep the excess atmospheric humidity under control. This operation does not necessarily have to be carried out every day, as only two openings per week may be enough.

However, it is necessary to avoid opening the protections on very cold days and in the presence of rain or fog, as the external atmospheric humidity may be higher than the internal one. After the winter, the protections are gradually ventilated (usually from March) until they are left completely open all day, perhaps closing them in the late afternoon if the nights are still cool, and then reopening them in the late morning. At the end of spring and during the summer the protections should always be left open, even at night.

Temperature

Another important element that affects the outcome of harvests during the winter is the temperature, which in the early hours of a cold morning with -5°C outside (when the thermal inversion causes both outside and inside temperatures to drop sharply) in an unheated greenhouse or tunnel can be as low as -3°C or at most 1 degree below zero.

In this type of protection, not having devices which heat the atmosphere, in order to defend the vegetables from the low temperatures it is necessary to use a veil of non-woven fabric (weighing at least 15-17 grams per square metre), to be spread directly on the cultivations, to be removed at the moment of the harvest and to be repositioned immediately afterwards; in case of very cold days, it is advisable to prepare two veils on the plants.

Always in order to protect the vegetables from the frost, if you live in particularly cold areas of the Centre-North, we suggest you to install inside the protections, especially in the tunnels, a second cover, formed by a smaller tunnel which has the function to further protect the cultivations from the cold and to limit the dripping on them. The drops of water, which form mainly on the inner side of the main cover, fall on the cover of the smaller tunnel and therefore not on the vegetables below. The crops can be protected from frost by installing small tunnels directly on the growing beds, with cover sheets made of transparent plastic film 0,07-0,1 micron thick. In this way the vegetables are grown under a double tunnel, inside which the temperature will be ideal especially for the cultivation of leafy vegetables such as lettuce and chicory, vegetables that could not give good harvests if grown in a normal unheated tunnel.

Watering

In order to ensure ideal growing conditions for vegetables grown under this type of protection, irrigation must also be taken care of, bearing in mind that it is always done indoors, with very different characteristics compared to open field conditions. After a rain, a cultivation in open field should not be irrigated, while under a greenhouse or a tunnel thing are different, because the protective cover does not allow the rain to reach the crops. For this reason, plants must always be guaranteed a moderately moist soil.

In addition, an unheated greenhouse or tunnel are often closed environments, where evapotranspiration is much lower than in the open field. For this reason, the frequency of irrigation and the amount of water supplied must also be reduced. Good rule, therefore, is to control the humidity of the soil before irrigating, operating according to the needs of the plants. The best hours to irrigate an unheated protection are in the morning, using water at room temperature (i.e. left to rest in bins for at least one day) so as not to cause thermal stress to the roots of the vegetables and provide the plants with a water reserve to draw on during the day.

Nicolas Campos

CHAPTER 11 - Pests and Diseases

Plant pests and diseases can affect even the most well-groomed flowers and vegetables and affect even the most experienced gardeners. Knowing how to recognise them is important and not complicated, not even for beginners.

Vegetable Diseases and Pests

All living organisms are subject to disease, both in the animal and plant kingdoms; diseases, of any kind and origin, stress the organism and can be the cause or trigger of other pathologies, in a chain of events that sometimes has some incredible.

Healthy and robust plants resist to the attack of diseases and parasites much better than weak or stressed ones, but this resistance is not an absolute guarantee; in fact, in spite of a correct cultivation, a careful weeding, the rotation of the crops and the selection of an increasing quantity of varieties resistant to diseases, even in the vegetable gardens cultivated with extreme care, problems of parasites and diseases can occur. Knowing how to diagnose the various diseases quickly and accurately is essential to be able to intervene as soon as possible with the right care, which very often involves the administration of chemical substances. Horticultural varieties are particularly delicate because unlike ornamental species they are very often destined for food consumption, with obvious health and ethical considerations.

Precautions when using agrochemicals

Always follow the manufacturer's instructions precisely, as regards dilution, application time and the period between the last application and the time of harvesting.

Keep these products tightly closed and labelled so that they are not accessible to children or animals. Never transfer them into beverage bottles. Spray on non-windy days so that the product does not fall on other plants or in nearby gardens, ponds, streams, springs or ditches. Never use for mixing or spraying containers already used for herbicides and never prepare more solution than is necessary, because then it is difficult to eliminate the excess without danger. Wash your hands and used instruments thoroughly after application.

These standards are almost always also present in the product leaflets.

Due to their nature, some chemicals must be used with even greater precautions. For example, calomel powder is poisonous and protective gloves must be worn while handling. Many substances can irritate the skin, eyes, nose and mouth; allergy sufferers should wear gloves, mask and goggles; some studies would also seem to indicate a carcinogenic risk of several substances, but at the moment there are no definite and incontrovertible data.

Using pesticides must always be done with extreme caution: not all insects and animals in the garden are harmful to plants, indeed there are some useful ones, think of pollinating insects (bees and the like), fundamental for the development of many fruits. They can be killed by pesticides, which is why they should not be used in excess and indiscriminately.

Pesticides and Fungicides

Fungicides are used to prevent infections while pesticides are used to combat infestations. There are many types of pesticides and they act in different ways. Those that act by contact (e.g. derris), directly affect insects: to kill the maximum amount of them, it is important to distribute these substances over the entire surface of the plant. After application they remain active for a relatively short period of time. Substances that act by translocation are absorbed by the plant and spread through the sap; they are very effective against lymph sucking insects. It is not necessary to spray the whole plant, but only the roots can be wetted. Most fungicides only prevent disease and should therefore be applied before the symptoms of an infection occur. Fungicides that act partially by translocation can now be found on the market. These products are partly absorbed by the tissues of the plant and act for a short period even if the infection is already in progress.

Methods of application

Chemicals can be purchased in the form of powders, soluble powders, sprays, ointments, pills, granules, aerosols. However, not all of them exist under each of these forms, nor are all forms effective for a certain type of disease or infestation. Most of these products are indicated in the text according to the active chemicals they contain and not according to name or brand. Always check that the most suitable active ingredients are contained; these are written on package labels or package leaflets.

Plant Diseases

Parsnip Cancer

It causes parsnip tissue rot. There are no effective remedies, but you can reduce the risk of an attack by growing the plants in a cool place, renewed every year, in a well tilled soil with a pH of 5.5-7.0.

Cabbage hernia (Plasmodiophora brassicae)

It deforms the roots and seriously compromises the development of all brassicas. This disease is more frequent in acidic soils; the pH of the soil can therefore be increased to 6,5-7,5 by distributing calcium cyanamide or calcium carbonate at a rate of 450 g/m2; maintain the degree of acidity at this level with small additions of the same substances in the following years. The 4% calomel dust incorporated into the soil at a rate of 45 g/m2 before sowing helps to combat hernia and is also effective against cabbage root fly. Seedlings can also be soaked in calomel powder or a benomyl solution as a preventive measure.

Alonate or charcoal spotting (Pseudomonas phaseolicola)

It is a bacterial infection that affects the seeds causing stains on the bean leaves. The stains are surrounded by a slightly coloured halo. There are no known effective remedies; diseased plants should be burned after harvesting.

Leaf spotting

It mainly affects brassicas, beets and beets by attacking the older leaves on which round, brown spots remain. Sometimes the affected tissues fall, and holes remain. It is a disease that worsens in the wetter seasons, especially in crowded crops or on brassicas that have grown too tender due to an excess of nitrogen fertilizers. The infected leaves must be removed and destroyed. How to prevent thinning plants and carry out careful crop rotation.

Bad asparagus wine (Rhizoctonia violacea)

It attacks the roots and the base of the asparagus growing wrapped around them in purplish filaments. Small round masses of fungal hyphae may also appear. With the death of the roots the vegetative apexes yellow and die. If the infection is light, the contaminated area can be isolated by introducing thick polyethylene sheets into the soil at a depth of 30 cm. If it is serious, leave the infected soil and transfer the cultivation elsewhere.

Seedling collar rot is favoured by conditions of stagnant or overcrowded air and the common use of unsterilized garden compound. The affected seedlings rot at collar height and collapse to the ground. As a prevention sowing in sterilized compost. Light infections can be kept under control by watering seedlings with captan, zineb or Chesthunt compost, after removing already dead seedlings, to avoid the risk of infection.

Onion rot (Botrytis allii)

It can destroy a large amount of onions stored for storage. A grey mould grows on or near the collar of the bulbs, making them soft and rotting. Then the large black spores of the fungus develop on the rotting tissues. Store only firm, dry bulbs in a cool, dry place with good ventilation all around. Check them often and discard those that begin to rot immediately. Since the infection can start from the seed, only buy good quality seedlings or seedlings already treated against rotting in a reputable shop. Sprinkle seeds and seedlings with benomyl powder before sowing or transplanting.

Black potato rot (Erwinia carotovora var. atroseptica)

It causes the early yellowing of the affected plants' foliage; the shoots fall due to rotting and blackening at the base, even if sometimes some stems can develop normally. The plant can die before tubers form, and those already formed have a slimy brown or grey rottenness inside them. Destroy any infected plant. If severely affected tubers are kept, they will rot, while those only slightly affected with no symptoms can go unnoticed but, if planted the following season, will transmit the infection.

Pedal and root rot

They are caused by different species of fungi that affect the roots and the stem base of young plants and kill them. As a prevention soak the seedlings in captan; at first symptoms water the plants immediately with a solution of captan, Chesthunt compound or zineb. For affected tomato plants tamp down sterile compost around the base. Burn diseased plants.

Moniliosis (Sclerotinia)

It affects the roots and the base of the stems of various plants, including carrots, cucumbers, Jerusalem artichokes, and the roots and tubers stored for storage. Burn the affected plants to prevent the infection from spreading to the rest of the soil through the large spores that form on diseased plants. Unfortunately, there are no suitable chemicals. Cleaning and rotation of affected crops are the only practical remedies that can be taken.

White onion mould (Sclerotium cepivorum)

It appears as a white felt at the base of the onions; it quickly causes the death of the leaves. Burn the plants as soon as you realize they are sick. As a prevention distribute 4% benomyl or calomel dust directly into the furrows before sowing or by spraying the plants with a benomyl solution when they have reached a height of 18-20 cm.

Grey mould (Botrytis cinerea)

It can affect most plants at any stage of development. It is favoured by overcrowding conditions and stagnant air; the stems, leaves or fruits affected rot quickly and are covered by a grey-brown mould. As a prevention sow well-spaced and thin out seedlings and plants. Ventilate greenhouse crops well and ensure that dead or rotting plant material is removed and burned. Spray wintering plants with thiram. If grey mould affects all greenhouse plants, fumigate with tecnazene.

Grey mould of legumes (Botrytis cinerea)

It causes discoloration of the leaves and stems of the broad beans and can attack wintering crops with serious consequences. Plants grown in acidic soils or those that grow too soft due to excess nitrogen fertilizers are most affected. As a prevention, sow rarely, distribute potash at a rate of 15 g/m2 before sowing in November and keep the pH of the soil between 6.5 and 7.0. In areas where grey mould is endemic, spray the still young foliage with a cupric fungicide before the symptoms of grey mould occur.

Hate or bad white

It attacks zucchini, cucumbers and other vegetables, especially when the roots do not have enough water. A white powder covers the stems and leaves. At first symptoms spray the affected plants with benomyl and, if necessary, repeat the treatment.

Peronospora

It can attack lettuce, onions, spinach and young brassicas. Sow well-spaced and thin out the seedlings in good time; if they are equally attached, remove all diseased leaves and spray with zineb or mancozeb. For the young cauliflower plants, you can also use dichlofluanid and on the other brassicas, onions and spinach the Bordeaux mush; for the lettuce is also good for the thiram.

Solanaceae downy mildew (Phytophthora infestans)

And a serious potato disease that also affects tomatoes. The leaves, stems and tubers of potatoes can be destroyed. To reduce the risk of infection, plant healthy tubers in holes at least 12 cm deep and tamp them down at the right time. Potatoes grown for the autumn harvest should also be sprayed with mancozeb, zineb or Bordeaux mush from July onwards. Cut and remove the stems before harvesting the tubers. In areas where this disease is widespread, plant varieties of potatoes that are resistant to downy mildew. Protect the tomatoes by spraying them in mid-summer immediately after topping with one of the products suitable for potatoes. If the weather is cool and humid, repeat the treatment every two or three weeks.

Common mange

It occurs mainly when the soil is arid, lacking in humus and in alkaline soils. A pH of 5.0-6.0 in the soil and an enrichment of the humus content reduce the incidence of this disease. In addition, the potatoes should be kept well irrigated, especially when the weather is dry. There are no effective chemicals against scabies.

Virosis

They cause leaf spots, deformations and often a stunted development of the plants. They attack mainly courgettes, celery, cucumbers and tomatoes, but also other vegetables. They are spread by aphids and nematodes; it is therefore necessary to keep these parasites under control and destroy the weeds, which serve as a receptacle. For infected plants there is no remedy: once the evil has been diagnosed the only thing to do is to burn them. Always wash your hands and tools very well after coming into contact with plants affected by virosis.

Vermin

Aphids

They infest most crops. In addition to the damage that aphids directly cause, they are carriers of virosis and promote the development of soot. Keep the plants under regular control; in case of attack nebulize with dimethoate, derris, formothion, malathion, menazon, pyrimidil or similar products. If harvesting should take place no more than one week after treatment, spray with derris. It is advisable to spray also the pumpkins only with derris or pyrethroids, otherwise they could be damaged; on the contrary, the peas and beans, if in flower, must be sprayed at dusk with pyrimidil, tolerated by the bees which are the main pollinators.

Root aphids (Pemphigus bursarius)

They can hit beans, lettuce and artichokes. Usually you do not notice the attack until the plants are infested. In case of serious infestation spray with malathion. As a prevention, distribute diazinon granules on the soil before sowing or transplanting.

Aleurodide or Greenhouse Whitefly (Trialeurodes vaporariorum)

It attacks brassicas, pumpkins, tomatoes and other vegetables and leaves soot deposits on the leaves. The cabbage whitefly is a species distinct from the greenhouse whitefly, but pyrethroid or pyrimiphos-methyl treatments are effective against both, spraying three or four times at seven-day intervals. In greenhouses, it is possible to resort to the integrated pest control by introducing the wasp Encarsia, thus avoiding the problem of the residues left by the pesticides and the habituation, but for most gardeners, unluckily, this method is not very practical.

Pole or land fleas (Phy/lotreta spp)

They are tiny beetles that infest the brassica seedlings in large numbers, devouring the leaves on which they leave small holes. Use derris, HCH or pirimiphos-methyl treatments. Plants are rarely damaged after they have passed the seedling stage.

Caterpillars

They attack cabbages and you must prevent them from penetrating to the heart, because it would be very difficult to reach them here. They can be removed by hand, if the number of plants is limited, or they can be treated with carbaryl, HCH or fenitrothion.

Snails, onyxes and centipedes

They can destroy seedlings and attack many developing vegetables. Against snails distribute along the rows of lures of metaldehyde or methiocarb. The latter is more effective against onisks and centipedes, but if the infestation is severe, it may be necessary to sprinkle seedlings with HCH powder.

Asparagus cryoceris (Crioceris asparagus)

It is a small yellow and black insect whose grey-black larvae can defoliate plants during the summer. Suppress them by spraying the asparagus with derris or pirimiphos-methyl as soon as you notice their presence.

Dorifora (Leptinotarsa decemlineata)

It is a parasite that affects the Solanaceae, especially potatoes and aubergines and, to a lesser extent, peppers and tomatoes. It attacks first the shoots and young leaves, then the other parts of the plants until they are completely defoliated. Afterwards, the plants can die. Soak affected plants with carbaryl.

Elaterides (Agriotes spp)

They can be found in large numbers in meadows and weed-infested areas. They attack the roots of many vegetables can seriously affect the quality of potatoes. Treat the soil when planting or sowing with diazinon or bromophos.

Celery fly (Phillophylla heraclei)

It lives in the leaves of celery, parsnip and some aromatic herbs. Against the most serious attacks nebulize the plants with malathion or dimethoate. If the infestation is light, however, remove the flies by hand and burn the affected leaves.

Carrot fly (Psila rosae)

It is the most harmful parasite of the carrot and attacks parsley, parsnip and celery. Plant growth is stunted, and secondary rot can develop in carrots already affected. Sow very seldom or use casing seeds by carefully arranging them so that you no longer need to thin out the plants afterwards, because the female of this pest is strongly attracted to the scent that is released from the carrot leaves during thinning. By sowing after the end of May you can avoid the first generation of larvae, but carrot flies are so common that it is advisable to sprinkle the sowing furrows with diazinon, bromophos or chlorpyrifos, in order to protect them for at least six to eight weeks. Nebulize with pirimiphos-methyl at the end of August carrots that are not harvested before autumn.

Onion fly (Chlortophila antiqua)

It attacks all plants belonging to the onion family. Young plants can be destroyed by the larvae and already developed bulbs are excavated by tunnels that make them inedible. During the early, more vulnerable stages of development, disinfect the soil with diazinon, bromophos or chlorpyrifos granules when sowing or transplanting.

Cabbage root fly (Chlortophila brassicae)

At the larva stage it can devastate the seedlings and young plants of many brassicas. Seeding furrows and planting soil should be treated in advance with diazinon, chlorpyrifos or bromophos. Against attacks on already well-established plants water abundantly with pirimiphos-methyl.

Onion Nematode (Ditylenchus dipsaci)

It attacks mainly plants belonging to the onion family, but also carrots, parsnips and beans. Nematodes are microscopic worm-like creatures that live inside the stems and leaves. Because of them the plant tissues become swollen and mushy and the plant does not take long to rot and die. For an amateur gardener there are no substances capable of suppressing this parasite and infested plants must be burned. Plants that can be attacked by nematodes, including some weeds, should not be grown in onion nematode infested soil for several years.

Golden potato nematode (Heterodera rostochiensis)

It lives in the roots of the potatoes and tomatoes and already by mid-summer the foliage is totally dead; the harvest is therefore very small. There are no chemicals available for amateur gardeners; crop rotation helps as a prevention, but if a soil is seriously infested, it may be necessary to stop growing potatoes. Some varieties of potatoes are resistant to a nematode species, Globodera rostochiensis, but none are so far resistant to G. pallida.

Nottue

They are caterpillars of different species of lepidoptera living in the ground. They feed on the roots and base of the stems of plants and attack most vegetables when they are still at an early stage, first withering and then dying. As a treatment, disinfect the soil with chlorpyrifos, dazino or bromophos before sowing or transplanting.

Red greenhouse spider (Tetranychus telarius)

It is a very common pest of vegetables grown in greenhouses and causes discoloration of the leaves and a halt in development. It has tiny dimensions: it is almost invisible to the naked eye. A humid atmosphere helps to keep away the red spiders, which thrive in hot and dry conditions, but to cope with the infestations spray the plants at seven-day intervals with malathion, dimethoate or pirimiphos-methyl. When using these substances on cucumbers be careful because they can damage the leaves; a less risky alternative is integrated pest control. Spray in the evening when it is less hot and make sure the roots of the plants are well moist.

Sitona leguminous plants (Sitona lineatus and S. limosus)

It feeds on the edge of the leaves of pea and bean plants. It is only necessary to use HCH or pirimiphos-methyl powder if seedlings are attached.

Pea turret (Cydia nigricana)

At the larva stage it seriously damages the peas, eating the fruit and compromising cultivation, especially in the case of late ripening varieties. Earlier varieties are generally not attacked because they flower before laying their eggs. Spray the peas that bloom between mid-June and mid-August, seven to ten days after flowering, with fenitrothion.

Pea tripe (Kakothrips pisivorus)

It is a very small and thin insect, brown-black or yellow, which sucks the sap from the leaves and pods of peas. This causes a silver-brown discoloration and the damaged pods can grow deformed and have only a few fruits. The most serious infestations occur especially in summer, when it is hot and dry. As a prevention nebulize with dimethoate, formothion or fenitrothion.

Birds

They can cause damage to crop throughout the year. Scarecrows and repellents are rarely effective; in some cases and only for short periods they can help, but if the problem of birds is constantly recurring, it is essential to use some kind of cage and protective net for plants and fruits so that the crops are not compromised.

CONCLUSION

Thank you for making it through to the end of this book, let's hope it was informative and able to provide you with all the tools you need to achieve your goals whatever they may be.

Greenhouse gardening has emerged as a great way to grow organic and genuine products to gain good health. Yet, not everyone gets the benefits of this wonderful process due to lack of knowledge of the process. This book has tried to bring all the important points on the forefront so that you can get all the benefits of greenhouse gardening without having to face the negative effects.

All you need to do is follow the information given in the book and stick to the adopted routine.

You can also get all the benefits of the process by following the simple steps given in the book.

I hope that this book can help you in achieving your goals.

Finally, if you found this book useful in any way, a review on Amazon is always appreciated!

THE OTHERS BOOKS by NICOLAS CAMPOS

GROWING MARIJUANA

A Complete Guide to Cultivate Medical Weed for Your Personal Use While at Home. How to Grow Marijuana Indoor & Outdoor.

COMPANION PLANTING

The Beginner's Guide to Organic Gardening. How to Use Chemical Free Methods to Reduce Pests and Combat Diseases. Use Crop Rotation to Increase Yield

Nicolas Campos

RAISED BED GARDENING

The Beginner's Guide to Everything You Need to Know to Start and Sustain a Thriving Garden. Grow Your Vegetables and Eat Healthy.

CPSIA information can be obtained
at www.ICGtesting.com
Printed in the USA
LVHW040728291020
669936LV00001B/67

9 781801 094795